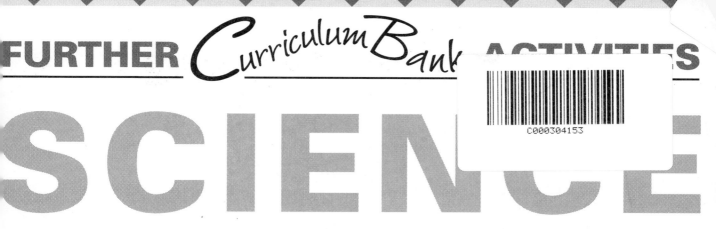

FURTHER *CurriculumBank* ACTIVITIES

SCIENCE

KEY STAGE TWO / SCOTTISH LEVELS C-E

SUZANNE KIRK

Published by Scholastic Ltd,
Villiers House,
Clarendon Avenue,
Leamington Spa,
Warwickshire CV32 5PR
Text © Suzanne Kirk
© 1999 Scholastic Ltd
1 2 3 4 5 6 7 8 9 0 9 0 1 2 3 4 5 6 7 8

Author
Suzanne Kirk

Editor
Joel Lane

Assistant editor
Clare Miller

Series designer
Rachel Warner

Designer
Rachel Warner

Illustrations
Maggie Downer

Cover illustration
Lesley Saddington

Scottish 5–14 links
Margaret Scott and Susan Gow

Acknowledgements
A.C. Cooper for photographs of the front cover illustrations
© 1999, A.C. Cooper.

British Library Cataloguing-in-Publication Data
A catalogue record for this book is available from
the British Library.

ISBN 0-590-53876-4

Contents

Introduction

Curriculum Bank Science (Key Stage 2/Scottish Levels C–E) provides a bank of activities. The book is divided into three sections, relating to 'Life Processes and Living Things' (Sc2), 'Materials and their Properties' (Sc3) and 'Physical Processes' (Sc4). Throughout the book, elements of 'Experimental and investigative science' (Sc1) are identified where appropriate, and many of the individual activities provide opportunities for children to undertake complete investigations.

Elements of the Introduction to the Science Programme of Study (Sc0) are also emphasized. 'Systematic Enquiry' and 'Communication' are relevant to all the activities in this book; the importance of 'Science in Everyday Life', 'The Nature of Scientific Ideas' and 'Health and Safety' are highlighted where appropriate.

The activities can easily be incorporated into any scheme of work. They also complement those described in the three original Curriculum Bank science books for Key Stage 2 (ISBN 0-590-53370-3, 0-590-53395-9 and 0-590-53369-X).

The overall aim of these activities is to develop children's interest in all aspects of science, to encourage them to ask questions and find solutions, to assist their understanding of difficult concepts and to build their confidence in this area of the curriculum. Many of the activities will help children to make connections, linking one idea with another and developing a wider picture of the world they live in.

In some activities, the emphasis is on practical involvement: children making their own discoveries through first-hand experience. Other activities emphasize the importance of using a wide range of secondary sources to obtain relevant information.

Investigations

In those activities (indicated by the ⬦ icon) which provide opportunities for a complete investigation, children are encouraged to:

▲ suggest ideas for testing;

▲ plan their test thoroughly – making predictions, devising a fair test, deciding what evidence they need to collect, and selecting equipment and materials;

▲ work accurately and methodically through the different stages – following their plan, making careful observations and accurate measurements (sometimes they will need to repeat these in order to check the accuracy of their results), and recording systematically;

▲ recognize the value of their results, and present them to share with others in a variety of ways – as charts, bar graphs, line graphs, information posters, accounts, strip cartoons, flow charts or instructions;

▲ draw conclusions – checking any predictions they have made against what they have discovered, and attempting explanations in the light of their scientific knowledge and experience.

It is important for children to develop a positive attitude towards science work. They should be curious, offer opinions, share their ideas and want to be involved in scientific discoveries. They need to understand the importance of working together co-operatively, and of persevering to complete a task successfully. Children should be encouraged to feel that they belong to the scientific world: that their ideas and efforts are worthwhile and their contributions valuable, both now and in the future.

Lesson plans

The structure for each activity is as follows:

Activity title box

The box at the beginning of each activity outlines the following key aspects:

▲ *Learning objective.* The learning objectives break down aspects of the Programme of Study for science into manageable teaching and learning chunks. They can easily be referenced to the National Curriculum for England and Wales and the Scottish National Guidelines 5–14 by using the overview grid on pages 13–16.

▲ *Class organization/Likely duration.* The icons ✝✝ and ⊕ indicate the suggested group sizes for each activity and the approximate amount of time required to complete it.

Previous skills/knowledge needed

This section gives information when it is necessary for the children to have acquired specific knowledge or skills prior to carrying out the activity.

Key background information

This section outlines the areas of study covered by the activity and gives a general background to the topic or theme, outlining the basic skills that will be developed and the way in which the activity will address the children's learning.

Preparation

This section indicates when it is necessary for the teacher to prime the pupils for the activity, to prepare materials or to set up a display or activity prior to the lesson.

Resources needed

All materials needed to carry out the activity, including photocopiable pages from this book, are listed here.

Vocabulary

Scientific words essential to the activity are listed here. They can be displayed, referred to during discussion and used by the children when recording.

What to do

Clear step-by-step instructions are given for carrying out the activity, including (where appropriate) suitable questions for the teacher to ask the children in order to help instigate discussion and stimulate investigation.

Suggestion(s) for extension/support

In these sections, ways of providing differentiation are suggested.

Assessment opportunities

Where appropriate, opportunities for ongoing teacher assessment of the children's work during or after the activity are highlighted.

Opportunities for IT

Where relevant IT work would strengthen an activity, appropriate possibilities are outlined with reference to suitable types of program.

Display ideas

Where they are relevant and innovative, display ideas are incorporated into the activity plans and illustrated with examples.

Reference to photocopiable sheets

Photocopiable activity sheets are provided for use with particular activities. Small reproductions of these are included in the appropriate lesson plans, together with notes on their use and (where appropriate) suggested answers to questions.

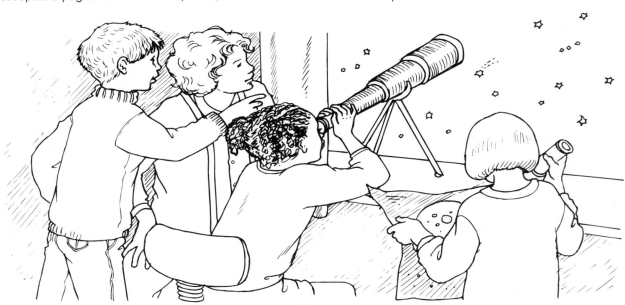

Overview Grid

This grid helps you to track the coverage of the Programme of Study for Science at Key Stage 2, or the Scottish National Guidelines for Environmental Studies 5–14 at Levels C–E, offered by the activities in this book. For each activity, the relevant statements from the National Curriculum for England and Wales and the Scottish 5–14 Guidelines are indicated (the latter references are given in italics).

Most of the activities in this book are linked to activities in the Curriculum Banks for Science at Key Stage 2/Scottish Levels C–E. These links are indicated by footnotes below the relevant activities, referring to the three relevant Curriculum Banks as follows: *Life processes and living things* as Bk 1; *Materials and their properties* as Bk 2; and *Physical processes* as Bk 3.

<table>
<tr><td colspan="5">ACTIVITY TITLE   LEARNING OBJECTIVE   POS/AO   CONTENT   PAGE</td></tr>
</table>

ACTIVITY TITLE	LEARNING OBJECTIVE	POS/AO	CONTENT	PAGE
What is the difference?	Living things can be grouped according to observable features. Careful observation is important when identifying plants and animals.	Sc2 4a/*Variety and characteristic features, Level C*	Recognizing the diversity among living things by using specimens, pictures and photocopiable page to observe differences between similar animals and plants.	14
Sorting living things, Bk 1 p.23				
Identifying habitats	Habitats are homes to living organisms. There are many types of habitat – some large, some small and some very small. Habitats need to be protected if the plants and animals which live there are to survive.	Sc2 5a, 5b/ *Interaction of living things with their environment Level C*	Identifying local habitats according to size; looking at the conditions they provide and the plants and animals which live there.	16
Habitats, Bk 1 p.28				
In the garden	Different animals find different food sources in a particular habitat. Scientific information can be obtained by reading a variety of texts.	Sc2 1a, 5b, 5c/ *as above*	Identifying from photocopiable text familiar garden animals and their food supply; recognizing predator and prey and devising food chains.	18
Feeding in animals, Bk 1 p.18; Animals and their environment, Bk 1 p.31; Food chains (1), Bk 1 p.34				
Living on a rocky shore	The animals and plants in a particular habitat are suited to their environment. Finding out about plants and animals helps us to understand how they live.	Sc2 5b/*as above*	Using photocopiable pages and reference material to find out how plants and animals living on a rocky shore are suited to their environment.	19
Plants and their environment, Bk 1 p.30; Animals and their environment, Bk 1 p.31				
Protecting habitats	Living organisms cannot survive if their habitats are changed or destroyed. What we know about habitats can help us to protect living things and their environment.	Sc2 5a, 5c/ *as above*	Discussing the effect of human activity on a specific habitat and the plant's and animals living there; considering an individual's responsibility towards protecting habitats.	21
Habitats, Bk 1 p.28				
What does a bird eat?	Different animals eat different foods. Asking questions helps us to find things out; sometimes we may be able to carry out an investigation.	Sc2 1a/*as above*	Grouping birds according to the food they eat, leading to possible investigation into the food preferences of garden birds.	22
Feeding in animals, Bk 1 p.18; Sorting living things, Bk 1 p.23				

(Left side vertical label: LIFE PROCESSES AND LIVING THINGS)

ACTIVITY TITLE	LEARNING OBJECTIVE	POS/AO	CONTENT	PAGE
Harmful micro-organisms	Some micro-organisms cause human diseases. Scientific ideas about diseases are based on evidence from experiments. Knowing about the activity of harmful micro-organisms can help us to avoid illness.	Sc2 5e/*Looking after oneself, Level C*	Using photocopiable text and other reference material to find out about harmful micro-organisms and the scientists whose discoveries have helped us fight disease. Preparing a code of hygiene.	23
Micro-organisms, Bk 1 p.37				
Useful micro-organisms	Some micro-organisms are beneficial and play an important part in bringing about decay. Making observations and drawing conclusions are important parts of an investigation.	Sc2 5e/*Interaction of living things with their environment, Level C*	Considering the importance of micro-organisms in the decomposition of waste materials. Planning and carrying out an investigation into the ideal conditions for micro-organism activity.	25
Micro-organisms, Bk 1 p.37				
Plants provide food	A variety of plants provide food for humans, and must be specially grown to feed the human population.	Sc2 1a, 1b, 2b, 5d/ *as above*	Identifying from specimens, pictures and photocopiable page the different parts of plants we use as food. Considering the amount of food required to feed the human population.	26
Food Bk, 1 p.68; How plants make food, Bk 1 p.56				
Plants need water	Plants need the right amount of water for healthy growth. Making careful measurements and collecting sufficient evidence are important parts of an investigation.	Sc2 3a/*Processes of life, Level C*	Planning and carrying out a class investigation to find out how much water seedlings need to grow well. Photocopiable page for structuring recording.	28
Plants and water, Bk 1 p.44				
Plants need light	Green plants need a daily supply of light for healthy growth. The results of a test help us to draw conclusions.	Sc2 3a/*Processes of life, Level D*	Observing plants deprived of light, discussing the effects and arranging further demonstrations.	30
Plants and light, Bk 1 p.45				
Hundreds of seeds	A flowering plant produces hundreds of seeds, making sure that some will germinate and grow to maturity in order to continue the species.	Sc2 3d/*as above*	Observing seed production in flowering plants; considering what happens to the hundreds of seeds many plants produce.	31
Seeds, Bk 1 p.60; Flowering plant life cycle, Bk 1 p.61				
The life of a tree	Trees, like other plants, have distinct stages and processes in their life cycle. Many species of trees are threatened by human activity.	Sc2 3d/*as above*	Looking at the life cycle of a tree; observing and recording the flowering and seed producing stages of a nearby tree.	32
Flowers, Bk 1 p.57; Seeds, Bk 1 p.60; Flowering plant life cycle, Bk 1 p.61				
A varied diet	To stay healthy, we need an adequate and varied diet. We can choose what to eat in order to be healthy.	Sc2 2b/*Looking after oneself, Level C*	Identifying and grouping different types of food; devising balanced lunchbox menus.	33
Food, Bk 1 p.68; Healthy diet, Bk 1 p.70				
Pulse rates	The heart beats faster during exercise to give the muscles a greater supply of blood. Sometimes observations and measurements need to be repeated if reliable evidence is to be collected during an investigation.	Sc2 2e/*Processes of life, Level D*	Recording resting pulse rates; planning and carrying out a class investigation into the effect of exercise on pulse rates.	34
Pulse rate, Bk 1 p.79				

ACTIVITY TITLE	LEARNING OBJECTIVE	POS/AO	CONTENT	PAGE
Skeletons	Many animals (including humans) have bony skeletons inside their bodies. Making comparisons helps us to understand how animals move.	Sc2 2f/*Processes of life, Level D*	Comparing the skeletons of different vertebrates; using photocopiable page to identify skeletons and relate structure to movement.	36
Our skeleton, Bk 1 p.74				
Growing bones	The bones which make up the skeleton grow as the animal grows. Accurate measurement is important when carrying out an investigation.	Sc2 2f/*as above*	Looking closely at specimens and pictures of bones. Planning and carrying out an investigation to compare bones in humans of different ages. Photocopiable page for structuring recording.	37
Our skeleton, Bk 1 p.74				
Moving muscles	Muscles are attached to the skeleton and contract to make bones move. Muscles work harder during exercise than when resting.	Sc2 2f/*as above*	Discussing the relationship between muscles and bones; moving and controlling muscles during exercise.	38
Muscles, Bk 1 p.76				
Growing and changing	Animals are born, grow, reach maturity, reproduce to continue the species, and eventually die. Humans are dependent on parental care for a relatively long time.	Sc2 2g/*as above*	Comparing three stages in the human life cycle: babyhood, childhood and young adult; comparing the early stages of the human life cycle with other animals.	39
Human life cycle, Bk 1 p.85				

MATERIALS AND THEIR PROPERTIES

ACTIVITY TITLE	LEARNING OBJECTIVE	POS/AO	CONTENT	PAGE
Using materials	Materials are useful for making particular objects because of their different properties. Some properties are more important than others when deciding what material to use.	Sc3 1a/*Materials from earth*	Using drawing on photocopiable page to identify materials, their properties and uses. Considering the advantages and disadvantages of different materials used for the same purpose.	41
Recognizing materials, Bk 2 p.16; Choosing the right material, Bk 2 p.37				
Comparing materials	To make a fair comparison of different materials, we need to carry out an investigation.	Sc3 1a/*as above*	Comparing materials; planning and carrying out a class investigation to compare the stretchiness of fabrics. Photocopiable page for guidance through investigation.	43
Recognizing materials, Bk 2 p.16				
Rocks of the earth	Rocks are used for a variety of purposes because of their characteristics. Information about rocks can be obtained from a variety of sources.	Sc3 1a, 1d/ *as above*	Examining rocks and building materials. Finding out from photocopiable text about the formation, characteristics and uses of rocks.	45
A close look at rocks, Bk 2 p.38; Rock hard, Bk 2 p.39				
Sieving soils	Soils consist of different knids of particles which can be separated by sieving.	Sc3 1e, 3a/ *as above*	Devising strategies for sieving soils so that different sized components can be compared.	46
Looking closely at soils, Bk 2 p.41				
Keeping warm, staying cool	The materials that keep things warm can also be used to keep things cool. An investigation is important for making comparisons.	Sc3 1b/*as above*	Discussing how to keep things warm or cool. Planning and carrying out a class investigation to compare materials which keep ice from melting. Considering the properties of thermal insulators.	48
Escaping heat, Bk 2 p.26; Holding on to heat, Bk 2 p.29; Keeping warm at home and school, Bk 2 p.30; Keeping ourselves warm, Bk 2 p.33; Insulating materials, Bk 2 p.90				

ACTIVITY TITLE	LEARNING OBJECTIVE	POS/AO	CONTENT	PAGE
Conducting and insulating	Some materials are useful as thermal insulators, others as thermal conductors. Materials (such as metals) which are good electrtical conductors are often good thermal conductors.	Sc3 1b, 1c/ *Properties and uses of energy, Level C*	Examining materials which are good thermal insulators or conductors and making comparisons with those which are good electrical insulators or conductors. Relating properties to uses.	49
Escaping heat, Bk 2 p.26; Travelling heat, Bk 2 p.27; Holding on to heat, Bk 2 p.29; Thermal insulators in the kitchen, Bk 2 p.32; Materials conducting electricity, Bk 2 p.34				
Solids or liquids?	There are differences between solids and liquids; however, solids which consist of small particles flow like liquids.	Sc3 1e/*On planet earth, Level E*	Identifying solids and liquids. Examining small particle solids which can behave like liquids; using photocopiable page to group solids, liquids, and solids behaving like liquids.	50
Solid, liquid or gas? Bk 2 p.44				
Solids to liquids, liquids to solids	Solids can change to liquids as the temperature rises; this is called melting. Liquids can become solids as the temperature falls; this is called solidifying or freezing. Both processes are reversible.	Sc3 2b, 2c, 2d/ *as above*	Identifying the processes of melting , freezing and solidifying and recognizing the changes of temperature involved; photocopiable page for recording.	52
Heating solid materials (1), Bk 2 p.55; Below zero, Bk 2 p.58; Freezing and melting, Bk 2 p.64				
Air all around	Air is a mixture of gases; it is all around us, and has weight. Making careful observations and repeating them helps in finding an explanation.	Sc3 1e/*as above*	Recognizing the presence and characteristics of air. Showing that air fills small spaces; recording observations on photocopiable page.	53
It's a gas, Bk 2 p.47; Bubbles, Bk 2 p.50				
Liquids to gases	Evaporation occurs when a liquid becomes a gas. Carrying out a fair test is the best way to obtain reliable evidence.	Sc3 2d, 2e/ *as above*	Planning and carrying out a class investigation into factors which affect the rate of evaporation with photocopiable page for recording planning.	55
Evaporation, Bk 2 p.66				
Changing state	Solid, liquid and gas are states in which materials exist. When a material changes from a solid to a liquid (for example), it has changed its state.	Sc3 1e, 2b, 2d/ *as above*	Reviewing changes of state and the processes involved; describing changes of state and processes in illustrations on photocopiable page.	56
Heating solid materials (1), Bk 2 p.55; Below zero, Bk 2 p.58; Freezing and melting, Bk 2 p.64; Evaporation, Bk 2 p.66; Condensation, Bk 2 p.70; Boiling and condensing, Bk 2 p.72				
How pure is water?	When a solid material dissolves in a liquid, it cannot be seen, however, it can be recovered by evaporating the liquid.	Sc3 2a, 2c, 2d, 3b, 3d/*as above*	Evaporating different samples of water to discover any dissolved materials; photocopiable page for recording predictions and observations.	57
Dissolving, Bk 2 p.66; Evaporation, Bk 2 p.66; Mixing mystery materials, Bk 2 p.69; Mixing materials with water, Bk 2 p.80; Recovering a dissolved material, Bk 2 p.83				
Investigating dissolving	Several factors can affect the rate at which solids dissolve in water. The results of an investigation can sometimes be usefully presented as a graph.	Sc3 2a, 3b/ *as above*	Planning and carrying out an investigation in small groups to discover the factors which affect the rate at which a solid dissolves in water.	59
Dissolving, Bk 2 p.66; Mixing materials with water, Bk 2 p.80; Heating and dissolving, Bk 2 p.95				

ACTIVITY TITLE	LEARNING OBJECTIVE	POS/AO	CONTENT	PAGE
Reversible and irreversible changes	Materials can change. Some changes can be reversed. When new materials are made, the change is usually irreversible.	Sc3 2c, 2d, 2f/ *Materials from earth, Level D*	Reviewing work on reversible changes by mapping processes which cause solids, liquids and gases to change state; vocabulary provided by photocopiable page.	60
Mixing materials, Bk 2 p.54; Heating solid materials (1), Bk 2 p.55; Heating solid materials (2), Bk 2 p.57; Freezing and melting, Bk 2 p.64; Dissolving, Bk 2 p.66; Evaporation, Bk 2 p.66; Mixing mystery materials, Bk 2 p.69; Condensation, Bk 2 p.70; Boiling and condensing, Bk 2 p.72; Burning materials, Bk 2 p.75				
Waste materials	Getting rid of our waste materials is a problem which we all can help to solve.	Sc2 5e; Sc3 1a, 2b, 2f/*as above*	Considering waste produced by unwanted materials; using photocopiable text and local information to find out about recycling. Recording problems and solutions on photocopiable page.	61
Sorting materials, Bk 2 p.14; Recognizing materials, Bk 2 p.16				

PHYSICAL PROCESSES

ACTIVITY TITLE	LEARNING OBJECTIVE	POS/AO	CONTENT	PAGE
The brightness of bulbs	A number of factors can affect the brightness of a bulb in a circuit. By testing one factor at a time, we can make comparisons.	Sc4 1a, 1c/ *Properties and uses of energy, Level D*	Reviewing circuits; planning and carrying out an investigation in pairs to change the brightness of a bulb in a circuit. Photocopiable page for recording predictions and observations.	63
Making a circuit, Bk 3 p.16; Resistance, Bk 3 p.24				
Changing the wires	The wires used in a circuit can affect the brightness of a bulb.	Sc3 1c; Sc4 1a, 1c, 1d/*as above*	Using symbols to represent circuits. Demonstrating in groups how changing the wires in a circuit can affect the brightness of a bulb.	65
Making a circuit, Bk 3 p.16; Resistance, Bk 3 p.24; Drawing circuits, Bk 3 p.28				
Magnetic forces	There are forces between magnets: they can attract and repel each other. By observing carefully, we can learn about these forces.	Sc4 2a/*Forces and their effects, Level D*	Using different types of magnets to explore magnetic forces.	66
Magnets, Bk 3 p.37				
Measuring forces	Forces can be measured; a force meter, sometimes called a newton meter, is used to measure forces.	Sc4 2f, 2h/*Forces and their effects, Level E*	Comparing sizes of forces; using a forcemeter to measure different forces.	67
What are forces? Bk 3 p.33				
Slide away	The size of the force required to start an object moving over different surfaces will vary. Collecting the right evidence during an investigation is important for answering a question.	Sc4 2f, 2h/ *as above*	Planning and carrying out an investigation in pairs to compare the different forces required to start an object moving over different surfaces. Photocopiable page for recording planning.	68
Gravity, Bk 3 p.44				
High and low friction	Sometimes friction is useful; sometimes it needs to be overcome.	Sc4 2c, 2f/*Forces and their effects, Level D*	Exploring examples of high and low friction; describing types of friction illustrated on photocopiable page.	70
Friction, Bk 3 p.41				

ACTIVITY TITLE	LEARNING OBJECTIVE	POS/AO	CONTENT	PAGE
Water resistance	An object moving through water is slowed down by the resisting force of the water. We can find out how water resistance affects objects of different shapes by carrying out an investigation.	Sc4 2c, 2f/*Forces and their effects, Level D*	Exploring examples which show the resisting force of water. Planning and carrying out a class investigation to compare the movement of different shapes through water; photocopiable page for recording observations and measurements.	71
The force of air	Air resistance is a force that slows objects moving through the air.	Sc4 2c, 2f/ *as above*	Exploring the resisting force of air.	72
Air resistance, Bk 3 p.46				
Spring is here	Because springs exert a force, they can be used in a variety of ways.	Sc4 2d, 2e/ *as above*	Exploring the forces exerted by springs. Identifying uses of springs; recording on photocopiable page.	73
Springs, Bk 3 p.50				
Stretching elastic bands	We can explore the force acting on an elastic band by measuring how much it stretches.	Sc4 2d/*as above*	Discussing the properties and uses of elastic bands. Exploring the force exerted on an elastic band as it is stretched.	74
Elastic power, Bk 3 p.48				
Balanced forces	When an object is at rest, the forces acting on it are balanced.	Sc4 2f, 2g/ *as above*	Reviewing different forces. Identifying balanced forces; using drawings on photocopiable page to show how balanced forces can be represented by equal sized arrows.	76
Weight in air and water	Objects weigh less in water than in air, because of the upward force of the water. We can use a force meter to demonstrate this.	Sc4 2b, 2f, 2h/ *Forces and their effects, Level E*	Using a forcemeter to show that objects weigh less in water than air; recording measurements on photocopiable page.	77
Weight, Bk 3 p.45				
Transparent and opaque	Transparent materials and objects allow a lot of light to pass through them, opaque materials and objects do not let any light pass through them.	Sc4 3a, 3b/ *Properties and uses of energy, Level C*	Investigating light passing through a range of materials; photocopiable page for recording predictions and observations.	79
How light travels, Bk 3 p.57; Transparency, Bk 3 p.58				
Light gets in your eyes	We see objects when light reflected from them enters our eyes.	Sc4 3a, 3d/ *Properties and uses of energy, Level D*	Using drawings on photocopiable page to show how light enters our eyes enabling us to see.	80
How we see, Bk 3 p.67				
Changing shadows	We can find out more about how the size and position of a shadow changes by carrying out an investigation.	Sc4 3a, 3b/ *as above*	Class or group investigation to discover the relationship between position of light source and object, and size of shadow; photocopiable page for recording planning.	82
Sizes of shadows, Bk 3 p.62				
Shadows and reflections	The differences between shadows and reflections tell us a lot about the behaviour of light.	Sc4 3a, 3b, 3c, 3d/ *as above*	Exploring and comparing shadows and reflections.	83
Shadows, Bk 3 p.59; Reflections, Bk 3 p.63				

NUMBER RELATIONSHIPS

ACTIVITY TITLE	LEARNING OBJECTIVE	POS/AO	CONTENT	PAGE
Travelling sounds	Sound vibrations can travel through various materials before they reach our ears.	Sc4 3e, 3g/ *Properties and uses of energy, Level C*	Exploring sounds travelling through different materials, solids, liquids and gases.	85
Sounds in school, Bk 3 p.70; Hearing sounds, Bk 3 p.77				
Keeping it quiet	Some materials are useful in preventing sound from reaching our ears. To make reliable comparisons, we must plan an investigation.	Sc4 3e, 3g/ *as above*	Identifying ways of minimizing sounds. Planning and carrying out a class or group investigation to find out which materials are effective in preventing sound from travelling.	86
Hearing sounds, Bk 3 p.77				
Tracking the sun's path	The Sun's apparent movement across the sky each day can be followed by observing the changes in light and shadows.	Sc4 4b, 4c/*Earth in space, Level C*	Demonstrating the apparent movement of the sun each day by observing patterns of light and shadow.	88
Tracking the sun, Bk 3 p.83				
Sunrise and sunset	The Sun rises in the east and sets in the west at predictable times. Graphs are useful for interpreting information.	Sc4 4b, 4c/*Earth in space, Level D*	Observing winter sunrises and sunsets. Using photocopiable page to interpret information and compare hours of daylight through the year.	89
Day and night, Bk 3 p.86; Earth's orbit, Bk 3 p.89				
Year to year	The Earth takes a fixed period of time to orbit the Sun; we call this period a year. Reference materials can help us to find information about areas of science which we cannot investigate for ourselves.	Sc4 4a, 4d/ *as above*	Demonstrating the movement of the earth in relation to the sun. Recording a year's events using photocopiable framework and photocopiable reference material.	91

Life processes and living things

As their interest in plants and animals grows, children need to develop a greater awareness of the relationships of living organisms – including themselves – with each other and with the world they inhabit. The activities in this chapter extend children's knowledge and widen their experience of plants and animals in their habitats; the dependence of animals on plants; and the importance of maintaining a healthy body. There are opportunities for first-hand exploration, investigation and use of secondary sources.

As they become aware of the amazing diversity of plants and animals and their dependence upon each other, the children will begin to understand the importance of a habitat to the organisms that live there, the pressures on the natural environment, and the need to protect and conserve habitats. To survive, every species needs suitable conditions under which to complete its life cycle. The school grounds (however small) can be developed as a useful resource to provide opportunities for first-hand exploration of a habitat (or several habitats) and the plants and animals which make their homes there.

Observing and growing plants raises children's awareness of the importance of plants in feeding the animal kingdom. The children should be encouraged to discover the conditions required by plants for healthy growth, and why it is essential for plants to grow well in order to survive (and provide animals with food).

Micro-organisms (living creatures too small to see with the naked eye) are also discussed. The vital role played by some micro-organisms in decomposing waste is investigated, and the threat to health by other micro-organisms (especially bacteria and viruses) is emphasized.

Through finding out more about their bodies – such as how muscles and bones work, and the importance of exercise and a varied diet – the children will learn to take responsibility for their own health, and will become more aware of the changes in themselves as they get older.

Where activities involve investigation, the children will have opportunities to ask questions, decide what evidence to collect, make careful measurements (repeating them to ensure accuracy), make comparisons and draw conclusions. Through exploring, investigating, making discoveries and acquiring information, the children will learn to appreciate the world in which they live and recognize their own responsibility to protect and conserve plants, animals and their habitats.

WHAT IS THE DIFFERENCE?

Living things can be grouped according to observable features. Careful observation is important when identifying plants and animals.

†† *Whole-class discussion followed by individual or paired work.*

🕑 *30 minutes for discussion, 45 minutes for individual work.*

Previous skills/knowledge needed
The children will need to be familiar with using hand lenses or other magnifying aids, and know that there is great diversity among plants and animals.

Key background information
Even among animals or plants within a single group, there is amazing diversity. There are more species of insects than of all other animals put together. The physical differences between one species and another provide the means of identifying them. It is important, for many reasons, that the diversity of plant and animal life is preserved. The Government has developed a national biodiversity strategy which involves local communities. Schools can liaise with councils, Wildlife Trusts and other environmental agencies in order to take part in projects such as monitoring wildlife sites and improving habitats in their locality.

Preparation
Collect or locate the following: two large pictures of animals from the same group, such as two birds or two mammals; two comparable plants, such as two pot plants or two school trees (find pictures if specimens are not available); other pairs of plant specimens for comparison, such as two different leaves, fruits, garden plants, flowers or weeds; other pairs of animal specimens, such as a stick insect and a woodlouse or a ladybird and a spider. Make one copy per child of photocopiable page 93, or page 94 where support is needed. Obtain some oak and holly leaves (or coloured pictures of them).

Resources needed
Pictures and specimens of paired animals and plants (see above); access for the children to a collection of books

and pictures showing a range of plants and animals; hand lenses and other magnifying aids; a camera; writing materials; photocopiable pages 93 and 94.

Vocabulary
Similarities, differences, in common, observing, observable, identify, identifying.

What to do
Show the class large pictures of two animals from the same group – for example, a duck and an owl. Ask the children to tell you how they know **from the pictures alone** that these creatures are both birds. They should mention the covering of feathers, the wings (but not flight), the two feet and the beak. Explain that although the duck and the owl are both birds and have important features in common, there are still many observable differences between them. Give the class a few minutes to jot down any differences they have noticed before discussing and listing them: the owl has a hooked beak, the duck a flat

Figure 1	
oak leaves	**holly leaves**
wavy edges	spiky edges
fairly thin and delicate	thick and tough
not shiny	shiny
lighter green	darker green

beak; the owl has clawed feet, the duck has webbed feet. The children may also recognize differences in the body and head shape and the colouring.

Repeat the same procedure with two plants, using actual specimens – such as two nearby trees or two classroom plants – if possible. Encourage the children to match the attributes of the two plants – for example: this tree has a smooth grey bark, this tree has a rough brown bark.

Make sure the children understand that they are identifying **observable** differences, and should only consider what they can actually see. When they are

observing living specimens, they can include habits and movements.

Provide copies of photocopiable page 93. Ask the children to record the differences between the bat and hedgehog, and then between the oak and holly leaves. (If specimens of leaves are available, colour and texture can also be considered.) Use a similar framework if other live specimens, models or pictures are available. Encourage the use of magnifying aids to identify detail when minibeasts, leaves, flowers or twigs are examined. Figure 1 shows an example of recording.

Suggestion(s) for extension
Some children could contact their local council and Wildlife Trust to find out what is being done to maintain biodiversity in their area, and how they might become involved. They could identify butterflies, amphibians, dragonflies or birds in their area and report these sightings, or ask for advice on creating a wildlife area within the school grounds.

Suggestion(s) for support
Children who have difficulty in completing photocopiable page 93 could work with copies of photocopiable page 94. Read the eight phrases on this page with the children, and encourage them to match each phrase to the appropriate picture. They should then cut out and sort the phrases and pictures. Help them to identify contrasting pairs.

Assessment opportunities
Focus on the children's observational skills: can they identify similarities and differences in appearance between similar organisms; can they use a hand lens to observe in greater detail? Assess their ability to record relevant information.

Opportunities for IT
The children can use a word-processing package to produce pairs of statements for display, selecting an appropriate font and size for the text.

Display ideas

The pictures used and the information generated by the activity can be displayed, so that the comparisons can be referred to and discussed. Photographs of the trees and pairs of pot plants, fruits, seeds and flowers can be arranged for the children to examine closely and make comparisons.

Other aspects of the PoS covered

Introduction (Sc0) 1a, b, c, d; 4a, c; 5a, b. Experimental and investigative science (Sc1) 2a, b.

Reference to photocopiable sheets

Photocopiable page 93 requires the children to compare two mammals and two leaves, recording their observations as notes beneath the pictures. Photocopiable page 94 provides an alternative activity for children who need support: following discussion, they can cut out the eight phrases and the pictures, then match each phrase to an appropriate picture.

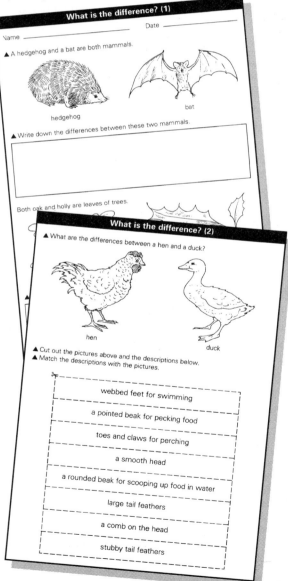

IDENTIFYING HABITATS

Habitats are homes to living organisms. There are many types of habitat – some large, some small and some very small. Habitats need to be protected if the plants and animals which live there are to survive.

†† *Whole-class introduction and discussion, then paired work.*

⏱ *30 minutes introductory activity; 60 minutes research and recording.*

Previous skills/knowledge needed

The children need to know what a habitat is (see below).

Key background information

Organism is a term which describes any living thing; it includes **plants, animals** and **fungi**. (Scientists now classify fungi as a separate group of organisms from plants and animals.)

A **habitat** is the place where any living thing (an organism) lives. A habitat provides food, water and protection; it allows the organism to live and grow, and to complete its **life cycle**. Habitats are diverse: they include huge areas such as deserts, oceans and icy wastes; smaller areas such as woods, fields and heathland; **mini-habitats** such as a tree, a flowerbed or a wall; and **micro-habitats** such as a leaf, the space under a stone or a pot of soil.

Preparation

Design a recording sheet similar to the one shown in Figure 2. Make two copies of it for each child: one to use out of doors and one for the final presentation of the information collected. Make appropriate arrangements (in line with your Local Authority Guidelines) if the children are going to look for habitats beyond the school grounds.

Figure 2	Identifying habitats		
A habitat provides a home for plants and animals. Describe 3 different habitats.			
Habitat	How does it provide light and shade?	What protection does the habitat provide?	What food and water supplies are available?

Resources needed

A recording sheet (see above); blank paper; a clipboard, hand lens and pencil for each child; pictures and other reference materials relating to a range of habitats. A camera would also be useful.

Vocabulary

Habitat, mini-habitat, micro-habitat, organism.

What to do

In the classroom, find out what the children already understand about habitats. Remind them of the requirements of living things: that they need a supply of food and water, shelter and protection, and the opportunity to reproduce. Ask the children what habitats they know of. Discuss how these can be grouped according to how big an area they cover. Introduce the terms **mini-habitat** and **micro-habitat**.

Explain that you want the class to catalogue the different habitats around their school (or in another area nearby). Arrange for some children to look for mini-habitats and others for micro-habitats. Give each child a hand lens, a recording sheet and some blank paper.

For each habitat they discover, encourage the children to record the conditions they think are available – for example, the amount of light or shade, the protection offered, and the food and water available. The children should try to find animals which occupy each habitat. Remind the children that habitats are homes: they should be disturbed as little as possible.

During the activity, make sure that the children are closely supervised. Encourage them to draw the habitats on blank paper, if there is time. If you have a camera, help the children to take photographs.

Discuss the information collected. (Figure 3 shows examples of filled-in record sheets.) Ask questions such as: *Were you surprised at the number of different habitats you discovered? Which creatures were found in a range of different habitats? Which were more specific in where they lived? Which habitat provided a home for the largest number of species? Were there any habitats which were endangered, perhaps by people walking over them or by vegetation dying? Which habitats are likely to change with the seasons? What will be the effect of leaves falling in the autumn, frozen ground in the winter, dense plant growth in the summer?*

Encourage the children to write up their information neatly on another copy of the record sheet. Collect all the information, forming a record of the habitats within the school grounds (or elsewhere) which can be used by others as reference material.

Suggestion(s) for extension

More able children could make a catalogue of habitats within the classroom and find out which living organisms are sharing the room with them. There might be spiders in the window-frames, greenfly on plants and woodlice or silverfish in damp cupboards. Similar research can be done at home.

Suggestion(s) for support

If necessary, guide children towards a specific habitat such as a rotting log where information can be collected easily. Provide help with recording.

Figure 3

Mini-habitat survey

habitat	conditions	animals and plants
1. garden next to playing field	sunny, plenty of plants and stones	slugs, hedgehog, frog, weeds
2. old wall at end of driveway	shady, plenty of holes	spiders, slugs, beetles, moss

Micro-habitat survey

habitat	conditions	animals and plants
leaf on silver birch tree	shady and sunny, water from leaf or rain	caterpillar spider
under a large stone	damp, plenty of moisture, darkness for hiding, cracks for sheltering	woodlice beetles worms

Assessment opportunities

From discussion and the recording work done, assess the children's understanding of 'organism' and 'habitat'. Assess the children's approach to scientific exploration by observing how they carry out research and record findings.

Opportunities for IT

The information collected can be stored on a permanent database, which can be updated yearly. As the database develops, the children can look for trends and changes over the seasons and from year to year, and understand the role they are playing in the monitoring and recording of valuable information.

Display ideas

The children's drawings and/or photographs, as well as similar pictures from magazines, can be displayed with appropriate labels, making a large pictorial representation of all the habitats and their characteristics or inhabitants. All the information collected by the children should be displayed, in order to emphasize its importance as research material.

Other aspects of the PoS covered

Introduction (Sc0)1a, b, c, d; 2a, d; 4a, c; 5a, b. Experimental and investigative science (Sc1) 2a, b.

IN THE GARDEN

Different animals find different food sources in a particular habitat. Scientific information can be obtained by reading a variety of texts.

†† *Whole-class introduction, followed by individual or paired research. This activity can be adapted for the Literacy Hour.*

🕐 *20 minutes reading and discussion; 30 minutes recording and research; 10 minutes reviewing; extra time for further research.*

Previous skills/knowledge needed

The children should be aware that different plants and animals can be found living within a particular habitat. They should have been introduced to the concept of food chains.

Key background information

For an organism to survive in a habitat, it must be able to find the food it needs there. Some plants and animals have very precise nutritional needs, and consequently are rarer than those with more general needs. For example, the caterpillars of the swallowtail butterfly feed only on the fenland plant known as milk parsley, and are thus limited to suitable parts of East Anglia; the caterpillars of peacock butterflies feed on nettles, and thus are widespread. Swallows, swifts and house martins feed on flying insects, and thus have to migrate when their food supplies diminish in colder weather.

Preparation

Make one copy per child of photocopiable page 95. Make a clue card for each of the ten creatures mentioned. Write the description on one side of the card and the name of the animal on the other side:

▲ small, spiky animal – hedgehog;
▲ long, juicy minibeasts – earthworms;
▲ dark, furry shapes – bats;
▲ five pairs of large eyes – frogs or toads;
▲ a feathery outline – owl;
▲ feathered flyers – house martins or swallows;
▲ hairy, black, wriggling creatures – caterpillars;
▲ tiny, green minibeasts – greenfly;
▲ spotted, red and black enemies [of greenfly] – ladybirds;
▲ soft, damp, legless bodies - slugs.

Resources needed

Photocopiable page 95; clue cards (see above); blank paper, pens or pencils; books or other reference materials providing information about the animals described and their feeding habits.

Vocabulary

Habitat, description, food supply, food chain, animal, minibeast, predator, prey.

What to do

Read the text on photocopiable page 95 with the children. Explain that several creatures are being described here. Ask them to write down the names of any animals they recognize. Give them a few minutes for this; then, using one or two examples, talk about how each of the descriptions represents a familiar garden animal. Tell them that ten animals are described.

Ask the children to record each description, the animal's name and its food on a chart (as in Figure 4). Sometimes the food supply is evident from the text; sometimes research will be needed to find the information. Provide a set of clue cards (see above) to which the children can refer as necessary.

Encourage the children to map any food chains they see developing, identifying predators and prey, and then choose one to research further. They could find out, for example, what else a hedgehog will eat, where it rests when not feeding, what sort of gardens will encourage it to stay and what would be detrimental to its survival – for example, pesticides or slug pellets (see Figure 5).

Figure 4

In the garden		
description	animal	food
small, spiky animal	hedgehog	earthworms
long juicy minibeasts	earthworms	rotting leaves and soil

Figure 5

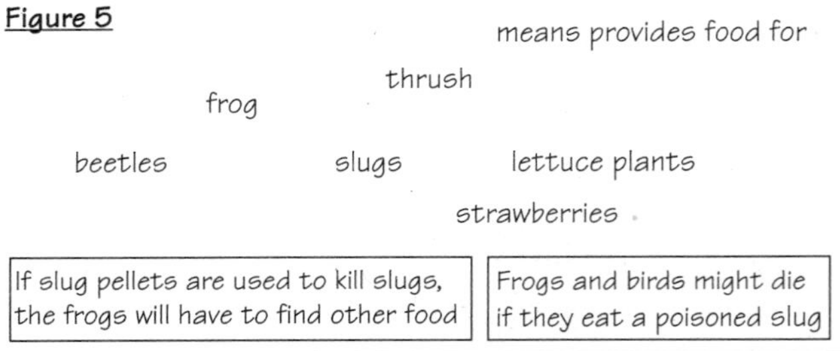

→ means provides food for

beetles → frog → thrush → slugs → lettuce plants → strawberries

If slug pellets are used to kill slugs, the frogs will have to find other food	Frogs and birds might die if they eat a poisoned slug

The children's findings can be presented, with drawings and diagrams, as a poster advertising a garden with a view to attracting a specific creature.

Suggestion(s) for extension

More confident readers could mark the verbs in the text which give clues to the activities of the creatures. Alternatively, they could research what each animal does as winter approaches and food becomes scarce. They could consider the school garden's habitat potential and how it might be improved.

Suggestion(s) for support

Less confident readers could use a version of photocopiable page 95 with the descriptions underlined and numbered. Encourage them to use the clue cards, and direct them towards appropriate books to help them find out what each animal feeds on.

Assessment opportunities

Assess the children's understanding of food chains: do they understand the relationship between predator and prey; can they draw a diagram, using arrows correctly, to represent a simple food chain? Assess their research skills and ability to present relevant findings.

Opportunities for IT

The children could use an appropriate software package to devise their recording chart and present information. They can use videos and CD-ROMs for research.

Display ideas

Use drawings or posters of animal activity in a garden by day and night. Arrange the children's work for others to see and display relevant books for further research.

Other aspects of the PoS covered

Introduction (Sc0) 1a,b,c,d; 2a,d; 4a,c.

Reference to photocopiable sheet

Photocopiable page 95 provides information about ten familiar animals which might visit a garden. The names of the animals are not given; the children are asked to try and identify as many as possible before using clue cards prepared by the teacher. They go on to record the animal's name, description and food on a chart, researching further information when necessary.

The sheet can be used for shared reading during the Literacy Hour. Discuss how adjectives are used; the different nouns used to describe the creatures (for example: minibeasts, shapes, flyers); and the verbs suggesting their activities.

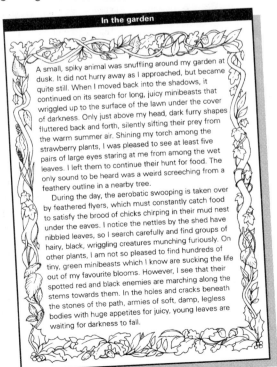

In the garden

A small, spiky animal was snuffling around my garden at dusk. It did not hurry away as I approached, but became quite still. When I moved back into the shadows, it continued on its search for long, juicy minibeasts that wriggled up to the surface of the lawn under the cover of darkness. Only just above my head, dark furry shapes fluttered back and forth, silently sifting their prey from the warm summer air. Shining my torch among the strawberry plants, I was pleased to see at least five pairs of large eyes staring at me from among the wet leaves. I left them to continue their hunt for food. The only sound to be heard was a weird screeching from a feathery outline in a nearby tree.

During the day, the aerobatic swooping is taken over by feathered flyers, which must constantly catch food to satisfy the brood of chicks chirping in their mud nest under the eaves. I notice the nettles by the shed have nibbled leaves, so I search carefully and find groups of hairy, black, wriggling creatures munching furiously. On other plants, I am not so pleased to find hundreds of tiny, green minibeasts which I know are sucking the life out of my favourite blooms. However, I see that their spotted red and black enemies are marching along the stems towards them. In the holes and cracks beneath the stones of the path, armies of soft, damp, legless bodies with huge appetites for juicy, young leaves are waiting for darkness to fall.

LIVING ON A ROCKY SHORE

The animals and plants in a particular habitat are suited to their environment. Finding out about plants and animals helps us to understand how they live.

†† *Whole-class discussion, followed by individual recording and research.*

⏲ *20 minutes discussion and drawing, 30–45 minutes recording.*

Previous skills/knowledge needed

The children will need to have identified a local habitat and considered why certain plants and animals live there.

Key background information

The **shoreline** is a habitat for many small animals. Some have soft bodies and drift with the tides; others have hard wave-resistant coverings (which also protect them from aerial predators); others hide among rocks. The sea is a provider of food, bringing twice-daily supplies of **plankton** (aquatic micro-organisms) and small fish to creatures (such as sea anemones) which live in the rock pools. Seaweeds are supported by water (some with the help of bladders along their fronds), and lie flat when the tide is out. **Limpets** graze on seaweeds; some other **molluscs** are carnivorous. The ecology of rocky coasts needs to be protected; it is important to remember, when visiting the seashore, that living organisms should not be moved or disturbed.

Preparation

Make one copy per child of each of photocopiable pages 96 and 97.

Resources needed

Photocopiable pages 96 and 97, pens and pencils; reference materials providing information about seashore habitats, animals and plants.

Vocabulary

Seashore, tide, waves, habitat, protect, protective, covered, exposed.

What to do

Find out which plants and animals the children associate with the seashore. Discuss the tides and the effect of the sea covering and uncovering this habitat twice every day. The plants and animals need to resist (or move with) the waves, and be able to survive for hours both underwater and exposed to the air.

Give out copies of photocopiable page 96. Use the 'low tide' drawing to identify a range of plants and animals. The seaweeds are lying flat; sea slaters (relatives of the woodlouse) and other small creatures scavenge beneath the plants; crabs hide among rocky pools; limpets fasten themselves firmly to rocks; sea anemones close up tightly. A sea bird with a long beak and long legs can probe the shallows and exposed sand for worms and molluscs.

Discuss the changes that the high tide will bring. As the tide comes in, bringing fresh supplies of plankton, limpets and crabs start to move around and forage; anemones sift the water with their tentacles; sea slaters burrow beneath rocks. Bladderwrack floats easily because of the air-filled sacs along its fronds, and the long, leathery kelp is lifted upright by the waves. The wading sea bird must wait until the tide is low again. Ask the children to complete the second drawing to show the changes which take place as the tide comes in. Encourage them to use reference materials.

Give out copies of photocopiable page 97. Ask the children to fill in this sheet, describing in detail the features of each plant and animal which is suited to a rocky shore habitat. Further reading can provide information about other plants and animals living in this type of habitat; these could be added to the 'high tide' drawing.

Suggestion(s) for extension

Ask a group of more able children to consider the similarities and differences between a garden and a stretch of seashore. They could investigate statements such as 'A hedgehog would be unhappy on a beach' and 'You are unlikely to see a wading sea bird in your garden.' Their ideas could be presented to the rest of the class.

Suggestion(s) for support

Less confident children could use the illustrations on photocopiable page 96 to help them complete photocopiable page 97. If appropriate, they could focus on one animal and one plant, drawing and annotating a large picture of each.

Assessment opportunities

From discussion and from their work on the two activity sheets, assess the children's understanding of a seashore habitat and how animals and plants are suited to this environment.

Opportunities for IT

The children could use CD-ROMs to collect information, perhaps cutting and pasting relevant text and pictures onto their own 'Factfile' page.

Display ideas

Use the children's drawings, paintings and models, together with posters, sand, shells and pebbles, to create a seashore display. Labels can be added to show how the living things are suited to their environment.

Other aspects of the PoS covered

Introduction (Sc0) 1c, d; 2a, d; 4a, c.

Reference to photocopiable sheets

Photocopiable page 96 shows a rocky shore at low tide, with various plants and animals. The children are asked to draw the same plants and animals as they might appear at high tide.

Photocopiable page 96 shows detailed pictures of the same plants and animals; the children can refer to it when completing page 97, but its main purpose is to stimulate observation of how each plant or animal is adapted to its environment. The seabird has long legs for wading, a long beak for probing in sand and between rocks, and wings to fly away when the tide comes in. The limpet has a tough shell to resist the waves and a strong muscular foot with which to cling to rocks. The anemone has a soft but sturdy body, and tentacles which can extract food from seawater and can be withdrawn when the tide is out. The crab has a hard protective shell and mouthparts to sift food from seawater, and can move quickly to hide among rocks when danger threatens. The sea slater is small and flattened in shape; it avoids light, hiding among rocks and beneath seaweed at low tide. Bladderwrack has strong, pliable fronds which are resistant to waves and drying, as well as air-filled sacs to lift the plant towards the light when in water. Kelp has very long, strong fronds which are tough and resistant to wave action and drying.

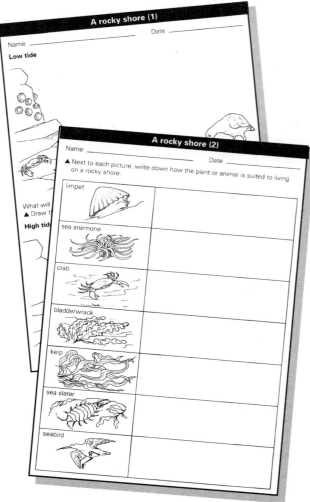

PROTECTING HABITATS

Living organisms cannot survive if their habitats are changed or destroyed. What we know about habitats can help us to protect living things and their environment.

✝✝ *Whole-class discussion, followed by individual or paired work.*

🕐 *60 minutes, plus extra time for further projects (optional).*

Previous skills/knowledge needed

The children should be aware of different habitats and their importance to the plants and animals which live there.

Key background information

The decline of many species is due to the loss of their habitat, usually caused by human activity. The forests roamed by huge creatures such as tigers and giant pandas are disappearing; wetland areas are being drained; many species are lost when rainforests are burned. Changes in agricultural methods have caused a decline in the skylark population; pollution from chemicals has destroyed life in inland waterways; building roads, houses and shopping centres uses up valuable land. Agenda 21, the global environmental strategy which developed from the Earth Summit in 1992, emphasizes the importance of children's involvement in environmental issues.

Preparation

Collect information about a local environmental issue, or develop an appropriate imaginary scenario (see below).

Resources needed

Newspaper cuttings and/or video footage relating to a local or national example of a changing habitat; reference materials relating to different habitats, the plants and animals which live there and the dangers they face from changes; writing and drawing materials.

Vocabulary

Habitat, protect, protecting, protection, change, events, consequences.

What to do

Create a scenario in which a habitat is about to suffer a change. This could be based partly or wholly on an actual case – if possible, one which is currently newsworthy. Possible examples include the effects of: building new houses on farmland; making a new road through woodland; open-cast mining; creating a new waste disposal site; an oil spill from a ship near the coast; filling in a pond; cutting down a tree; removing a hedgerow; contamination of a stream; children causing damage at local sites.

Consider the wildlife which lives in this habitat – both plants and animals. Now discuss the consequences of a major change. *Will the animals' food and water supply still be available? Is there anywhere to shelter? Can any of the animals find another similar habitat, or a different type of habitat, by themselves – or with help? Is there anywhere else for them to go? Will the species survive?*

Encourage the children to become involved in the dilemma and to consider what they could do to help protect the habitat. They might design a poster to make others aware of the issue, or write a letter expressing their concerns to a local newspaper, the council or a wildlife group. Remind them to set out their points clearly and to explain the effects that the destruction of the habitat will have. Point out that children have a special role to play in helping to protect the environment.

As a follow-up project, the children can plan and (if possible) create a new habitat in the school grounds. This could involve planting a tree; building a log pile, a small wall or a beetle bank; making a garden or a pond; or allowing an area of grass to grow long.

Suggestion(s) for extension

Keen children could find out about current projects to improve the environment by writing to their local council, to local conservation groups which specialize in protecting a particular animal (such as bats, hedgehogs, moths or frogs), or to agencies involved in keeping waterways clean, protecting green areas or planting community forests.

Suggestion(s) for support

Children who find this work difficult could be helped to create a concept map, starting with a habitat such as a pond, and using words or pictures to demonstrate the consequences of a sudden or gradual change.

Assessment opportunities

Assess how well the children are able to apply their scientific knowledge of habitats to a real situation. Can they present a reasoned argument when writing their letters?

Opportunities for IT

The children could use the Internet to find information on current issues relating to habitat loss. They could use a word-processing package to write letters, and use a desktop publishing package to design posters.

Display ideas

The children's posters and letters (or copies of them) can be used to share the information. The value of the children's work can be demonstrated by displaying it in the local library or a shop window.

Other aspects of the PoS covered

Introduction (Sc0) 1c, d; 2a, d; 4a, c.

WHAT DOES A BIRD EAT?

Different animals eat different foods. Asking questions helps us to find things out; sometimes we may be able to carry out an investigation.

†† *Whole-class introduction, followed by individual or paired work.*

⏲ *30 minutes for initial activity, 45 minutes for presenting work; extra time for any investigative work which develops.*

Previous skills/knowledge needed

The children should know that all animals, including themselves, require the correct type and amount of food in order to grow and be active.

Key background information

Some creatures are very specific in what they eat, perhaps feeding on only one type of plant; others are more general in their eating habits, and may consume a range of different foods.

Preparation

Prepare an alphabetical list of various birds (see 'Suggestion(s) for support' below).

Resources needed

A range of reference materials about birds and their feeding habits; writing and drawing materials. A bird table or feeding station would be useful.

Vocabulary

Different, difference, food, feeding.

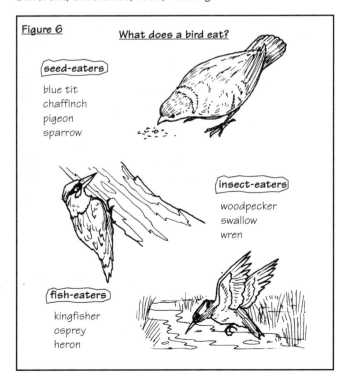

Figure 6   What does a bird eat?

seed-eaters
blue tit
chaffinch
pigeon
sparrow

insect-eaters
woodpecker
swallow
wren

fish-eaters
kingfisher
osprey
heron

What to do

Allow about five minutes for the children, working individually or in pairs, to write down the names of as many birds as they can think of. Then ask each child to contribute one bird from their list, so that everyone can add to their own lists as necessary. Next, discuss the types of food that birds are known to eat: seeds, nuts, breadcrumbs, fish, caterpillars, earthworms, beetles, mice, other birds, snails and so on. Agree on a way of grouping these types of food so that the birds can be put into categories according to their diet – for example: seeds and nuts; insects and other minibeasts; leaves; fish; small mammals and other birds. Other categories might include birds which scavenge and birds which eat several different foods (omnivores).

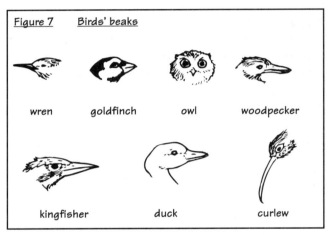

Figure 7   Birds' beaks

wren   goldfinch   owl   woodpecker

kingfisher   duck   curlew

Ask the children to sort their lists of birds according to these categories, using appropriate books and other reference materials. They can then make a pictorial chart to show the results. (Figure 6 shows an example.) Encourage the children to look for any similarities between the birds in a group. For example, they may notice that birds which feed on small mammals and birds have hooked beaks and sharp claws, while those which eat insects have pointed beaks. (See Figure 7.)

Ask the children to consider how they could discover the food preferences of birds which visit a bird table. Suggestions could lead to an investigation being carried out during the winter months. The children can set up a feeding station close to a window; provide different types of food (such as peanuts, sunflower seeds, fat and grain) at the same time each day; and observe and monitor the birds visiting and the foods they eat. A sheet of dark paper fastened to the window, with cut-out viewing holes, will screen the children's activity from the birds.

Suggestion(s) for extension

Write the words *carnivores, insectivores, omnivores, scavengers, vegetarians* and *predators* on individual cards. Ask a group of more able children to find the meanings of these terms using a dictionary or glossary, then write them on the backs of the cards to be used for class reference.

Suggestion(s) for support

Provide an alphabetical list of birds to assist those children who need extra help with spelling and reading. Make sure that appropriate, easy-to-use reference material is available.

Assessment opportunities

Assess the children's ability to sort, categorize and present information, and to put forward ideas for investigation.

Opportunities for IT

The children could enter their data about birds and their feeding habits into a database set up by the teacher. They could cross-reference information in different fields – for example, FOOD and BEAK or FOOD and HABITAT.

Display ideas

The children's drawings can be displayed, along with pictures from reference materials, to demonstrate the different types of food preferred by different birds. Use the display to link physical appearance and habitat to feeding habits. Add questions such as: *Why didn't a kingfisher visit our bird table? Have you ever seen a swallow eating a worm? Can a duck crack a nut?*

Other aspects of the PoS covered

Introduction (Sc0) 1a, b, c, d; 2a; 4a, c. Experimental and investigative science (Sc1) 1a (and other aspects if an investigation is carried out).

HARMFUL MICRO-ORGANISMS

Some micro-organisms cause diseases in humans. Scientific ideas about diseases are based on evidence from experiments. Knowing about the activity of harmful micro-organisms can help us to avoid illness.

✚✚ *Whole-class discussion, followed by individual or paired work.*

🕑 *30–40 minutes for reading and discussion, 45 minutes for individual work; further time for artwork, a visit or a talk. This activity could be adapted for the Literacy Hour.*

Previous skills/knowledge needed

It will be helpful if the children already understand that micro-organisms are very small living things which can only be seen through a powerful microscope; and that many micro-organisms are beneficial to humans, but others are harmful.

Key background information

Micro-organisms include **bacteria**, **viruses** and some **fungi**.

Louis Pasteur lived from 1822 to 1895. He was a meticulous investigator, starting his career as a chemist before becoming fascinated by the activity of micro-organisms. His experiments disproved the idea of 'spontaneous generation': they showed that infection and fermentation were caused by airborne micro-organisms. Pasteur's work led to the **germ** theory of diseases: that each disease is caused by a specific micro-organism. This led to the discovery of **vaccines** which could be used to prevent diseases. Pasteur is famous for his original observations and precise experimental method. He is quoted as saying: 'In the field of experimentation, chance favours only the prepared mind.'

Preparation

Make one copy per child of photocopiable page 98. If appropriate, arrange for the children to visit a health centre or for a professional health worker to talk to the class. Ask the kitchen staff whether they are willing to show groups of children their working areas and to explain their methods for maintaining hygiene.

Resources needed

Photocopiable page 98; reference materials about relevant scientists, including Edward Jenner, Louis Pasteur and Joseph Lister; information relating to health, hygiene and common illnesses; large sheets of paper, writing and drawing materials.

Vocabulary

Micro-organisms, harmful, illness, disease, evidence, prevent, prevention, hygiene.

What to do

Remind the children of the existence of micro-organisms. Find out how much they know about what makes them ill and how diseases are spread.

Read through photocopiable page 98 with the children, discussing the questions it raises:

▲ *Why did people not know what caused illnesses?*

▲ *What did Pasteur and other scientists need to do to prove that micro-organisms feed, grow and reproduce?*

▲ *What foods can be infected by micro-organisms?*

▲ *What should we do to keep our food free of micro-organisms?* (Heat kills micro-organisms and cold temperatures slow their growth. Food should be touched only with clean hands and kept in a clean place.)

▲ *What personal habits are important if we are to keep our bodies healthy?* (Washing our hands to avoid stomach upsets, cleaning our teeth to prevent decay.)

▲ *What precautions are taken in hospitals to minimize infection during treatment and operations?*

▲ *How are diseases such as chickenpox, measles and rubella spread?*

Use the discoveries of Louis Pasteur as an example of scientific method, pointing out the importance of doing investigations which produce evidence to prove or disprove an idea.

Ask the children (working individually or in pairs) to prepare an information poster on hygiene for younger children to refer to when preparing food. Points should include: washing hands before touching food and after using the toilet; keeping food in the fridge; separating raw and cooked foods; cooking food properly; washing fruit before eating it; keeping surfaces, dishcloths and tea towels clean.

Suggestion(s) for extension

More able children could find out about **vaccination** as a method of fighting the micro-organisms which cause disease.

Suggestion(s) for support

Write out a simple hygiene code, mixing up the words within each statement. Children who have difficulty with writing can rearrange the words and copy out the statements to make their own poster.

Assessment opportunities

Assess the children's grasp of scientific ideas when they are explaining the causes of disease. Do they understand that our knowledge of diseases and illnesses depends on scientific evidence? Can they relate their scientific knowledge to their own health? Are they aware that restricting the activity of harmful micro-organisms helps them to prevent themselves from becoming ill?

Opportunities for IT

The children could use encyclopedia CD-ROMs to find out about the relevant scientists. They could create their posters using a DTP package; the illustrations could be created using an art software package, scanned in from the children's drawings or taken from a clip art file.

Display ideas

The children could invent benevolent or malevolent cartoon characters (Chris Clean, Barry the Bug) to draw attention to their ideas for avoiding infection. They could display profiles of great medical scientists, with drawings and photographs.

Other aspects of the PoS covered

Introduction (Sc0) 1a, c, d; 2a, b, c; 3b; 4a, c; 5a, b.

Reference to photocopiable sheet

Photocopiable page 98 can be used for shared reading during the Literacy Hour. Reference can be made to unfamiliar vocabulary, the meaning of **micro** in the words 'micro-organisms', 'microbe' and 'microscope', and the different names given to micro-organisms. Ask appropriate questions to help the children find information on the page.

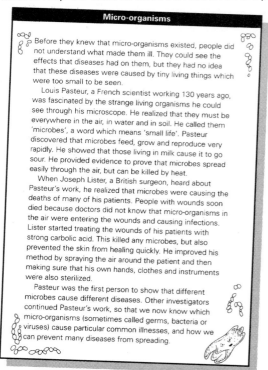

Micro-organisms

Before they knew that micro-organisms existed, people did not understand what made them ill. They could see the effects that diseases had on them, but they had no idea that these diseases were caused by tiny living things which were too small to be seen.

Louis Pasteur, a French scientist working 130 years ago, was fascinated by the strange living organisms he could see through his microscope. He realized that they must be everywhere in the air, in water and in soil. He called them 'microbes', a word which means 'small life'. Pasteur discovered that microbes feed, grow and reproduce very rapidly. He showed that those living in milk cause it to go sour. He provided evidence to prove that microbes spread easily through the air, but can be killed by heat.

When Joseph Lister, a British surgeon, heard about Pasteur's work, he realized that microbes were causing the deaths of many of his patients. People with wounds soon died because doctors did not know that micro-organisms in the air were entering the wounds and causing infections. Lister started treating the wounds of his patients with strong carbolic acid. This killed any microbes, but also prevented the skin from healing quickly. He improved his method by spraying the air around the patient and then making sure that his own hands, clothes and instruments were also sterilized.

Pasteur was the first person to show that different microbes cause different diseases. Other investigators continued Pasteur's work, so that we now know which micro-organisms (sometimes called germs, bacteria or viruses) cause particular common illnesses, and how we can prevent many diseases from spreading.

USEFUL MICRO-ORGANISMS

Some micro-organisms are beneficial and play an important part in bringing about decay. Making observations and drawing conclusions are important parts of an investigation.

✝✝ *Whole-class introductory activity; investigation as a class or in groups.*

🕐 *30 minutes activity; 60 minutes for planning investigation; further time for regular observations and presenting results.*

⚠ *Provide disposable gloves for collecting rubbish. Bags of decomposing grass or leaves must remain unopened and be disposed of at the end of the activity.*

Previous skills/knowledge needed

The children should be aware that micro-organisms exist and know that some micro-organisms are harmful, but there are others that we cannot live without.

Key background information

Some types of micro-organisms are **decomposers** that play a valuable role in the decay of natural materials and much of the rubbish we produce. **Nutrients** are released back into the soil as leaves, branches, animal waste and remains, paper and some plastics and fabrics are decomposed. However, this only occurs if conditions are suitable for micro-organism activity: warmth, dampness and the presence of air are essential. Materials which are readily attacked by micro-organisms are said to be **biodegradable**. The decay of soft natural materials begins as soon as conditions are suitable and proceeds rapidly; paper and some fabrics take longer; metals and some plastics resist decay indefinitely.

Preparation

Collect a variety of discarded rubbish, including leaves, vegetable peelings, grass cuttings, a piece of wood, a plastic bag, a crisp packet, a drinks can, an item of clothing, a shoe, a glass bottle, a plastic bottle and a piece of metal. Give each item a number. Prepare recording sheets as appropriate for the investigation.

Resources needed

A collection of rubbish (see above); clear plastic bags and ties; access to a refrigerator or cold store (if possible).

Vocabulary

Micro-organisms, useful, decompose, decomposition, decay, waste, dispose, disposal, conditions, natural, manufactured.

What to do

Remind the children about micro-organisms, and tell them that some types perform a valuable role in the process of decay. Discuss the importance of micro-organism activity in reducing dead and waste material, much of it unpleasant, which would otherwise pile up forever.

Display the items of numbered rubbish. Ask the children to predict and write down the order in which these items will decay (be decomposed). Discuss the children's ideas and reach a class decision. *Why do you think the leaves will rot away more quickly than a plastic bag? What evidence do you have for your idea?* (Perhaps they have noticed plastic litter lingering while leaves seem to disappear.) *What qualities do manufactured materials possess which helps to prevent action by micro-organisms?* (They are strong and durable.) *What happens to discarded glass and metal?*

Consider the rate at which micro-organisms attack waste, and the problem of the disposal of various different kinds of waste. **Biodegradable** waste is easy to dispose of, but cannot be allowed to decay in places where it might attract rats or cause disease. **Non-biodegradable** waste is much harder to dispose of. Suggest that the children look out for labels on packaging and bring in biodegradable items for display.

Organize the class into groups. Encourage the children to use their knowledge and experience to consider the conditions in which micro-organisms will work best. Ask them to suggest and plan a safe investigation, using natural materials, which would provide evidence to confirm their ideas. One group might choose to test dry, damp and wet conditions; another hot, warm and cold conditions. Grass cuttings or leaves can be used; these should be contained in clear, loosely tied plastic bags, which should be disposed of unopened at the end of the investigation.

Provide a framework to guide the children through the planning process:

1. What do you want to find out?

2. What are your predictions? What do you think will happen?

3. What evidence will you be looking for? How often will you make observations? How will you record your observations?

4. How will you make sure the test is fair? What will you change? What will you keep the same?

Make sure that the children carry out the test efficiently and in a scientific manner, recording their observations in detail on a prepared chart, making comparisons and following their plan. They should complete their investigation by presenting their results. Point out that the collecting of evidence is the most important part of the investigation: if the test is fair, then the evidence is valuable. The children should attempt to explain what they have found out, checking the evidence against their predictions and drawing conclusions.

Suggestion(s) for extension

More confident children could find out about making compost from vegetable peelings and garden waste, inviting a local gardener to help them create a compost heap in the school grounds. They could write to the council in order to find out about the problems involved in disposing of local rubbish, whether recycling is encouraged and where the nearest landfill site is.

Suggestion(s) for support

Some children may need to be guided through the investigation step by step. Provide a sequence of questions and a prepared recording sheet, so that these children can work confidently and scientifically.

Assessment opportunities

Assess the children's scientific approach when they carry out a complete investigation: do they observe carefully and consistently; do they make accurate recordings? Focus on their ability to plan a fair test and to draw conclusions.

Opportunities for IT

The children can use a word-processing package to write an account of their investigation and record their results in the form of a table.

Display ideas

The items of rubbish from the activity can be arranged with labels to explain the ordering. The planning and results of the investigation can be displayed for future reference. The children could design posters advertising the 'services' of useful micro-organisms.

Other aspects of the PoS covered

Introduction (Sc0) 1a, b, c, d; 2a, b, c, d; 3a, b; 4 a, c; 5a, b. Experimental and investigative science (Sc1) 1a, b, c, d; 2b; 3b, c, d, e.

PLANTS PROVIDE FOOD

A variety of plants provide food for humans, and must be specially grown to feed the human population.

✝✝ *Whole-class discussion, including some individual work.*

🕐 *60 minutes (plus extra time if visits are arranged or plants are grown).*

⚠ *Any preparation of food which might result from this activity must take place only under strict hygienic conditions. The children should be warned that not all plants are suitable as food, and many have parts which are poisonous.*

Previous skills/knowledge needed

The children need to know that there is a wide variety of plants, and that most of them make their own food.

Key background information

Green plants make their own food by **photosynthesis**, using sunlight, water, carbon dioxide and the pigment **chlorophyll** (in the leaves). The food enables the plant to function and grow; some food is stored in the cells within the plant. Animals utilize this food by eating plants, or by eating animals which have fed on plants.

Some human food is gathered from the wild, but most is specially cultivated. Many different fruits are eaten, as well as seeds, leaves, stems, flowers, buds and roots. Potatoes do not grow on the root of the plant, but on a swollen underground stem. During this activity, remind the children that parts of some plants are not only inedible but poisonous.

Preparation

Collect examples or pictures of edible plant parts, such as: carrots and turnips (roots); celery and rhubarb (stems); lettuce and cabbage (leaves); cauliflower and broccoli (flowers); tomatoes and melons (fruits); peas, beans and nuts (seeds); onions (bulbs). Arrange for the class to visit a market or greengrocer, or to grow food if appropriate. Make some copies of photocopiable page 99 (see 'Suggestion(s) for support').

Resources needed

Examples or pictures of plant foods (see above; reference materials relating to plant foods; photocopiable page 99; paper, drawing and writing materials. If food is to be grown, you will need seeds, peat-free compost, plant pots and grow-bags.

Vocabulary

Food, feeding, fruit, vegetable, crop, flower, seed, leaf, stem, root, bulb.

What to do

If possible, visit a market or greengrocer. Introduce a range of plant foods to the class by bringing in different fruits and vegetables, perhaps asking the children to add further items to the collection. Use pictures or a video to show other plants that we use as foods. Examine the foods and discuss the different parts of plants that are eaten. Sort them into groups according to what part of the plant they are. Ask the children (working individually) to record this information on a small poster using labelled drawings and appropriate statements.

Consider the huge amounts of food which must be grown to feed everyone, and the scientific research which is needed to provide good crops. Do a quick survey to see how many bananas (for example) the class consumes each week. On this basis, estimate the number for the whole school. Encourage the children to think about where all these bananas come from and the need to make sure of a good crop. Discuss the different areas of science which farmers rely on in order to produce the best crops by improving the soil, growing the most suitable crops for the climate and choosing disease-resistant crops.

If possible, follow up this activity by arranging a visit to a farm, market garden or allotment. Grow some food by planting quick-growing seeds such as radish or beansprouts. Peas, beans, tomatoes and pumpkins can be grown in grow-bags during the summer term. A potato planted in a large pot or plastic bucket (with a drainage hole) will yield a crop if kept in a courtyard or porch.

Suggestion(s) for extension

More able children could plan a menu to include food from each part of a plant. They could find out which plant parts are eaten by other cultures, and how they are grown.

Suggestion(s) for support

Children who have difficulty with recording can use photocopiable page 99 as a framework. They can use the list of words at the bottom of the sheet to identify the part of each plant that is used as food.

Assessment opportunities

Focus on the children's knowledge of the parts of a plant, and their understanding of the need for large quantities of food to be grown. Photocopiable page 99 could be used as an assessment sheet.

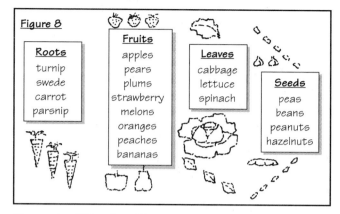

Figure 8

Roots
turnip
swede
carrot
parsnip

Fruits
apples
pears
plums
strawberry
melons
oranges
peaches
bananas

Leaves
cabbage
lettuce
spinach

Seeds
peas
beans
peanuts
hazelnuts

Opportunities for IT

When making their posters, the children can use appropriate DTP and graphics software to create designs, labels and lists.

Display ideas

During art lessons, the children could make a decorative background of fruit and vegetable designs or prints to accompany lists of plant foods (see Figure 8). They could design posters to promote awareness of plant foods.

Other aspects of the PoS covered

Introduction (Sc0) 1a, c, d; 2b; 4a, c; 5a, b.

Reference to photocopiable sheet

Photocopiable page 99 can be used for recording (see 'Suggestion(s) for support'), or to assess knowledge of the parts of plants that we use as foods.

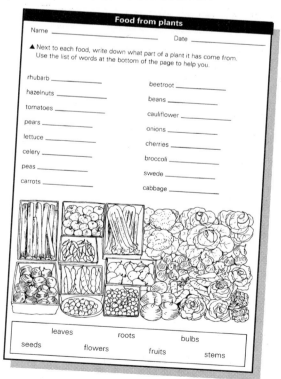

Food from plants

Name _____

Date _____

▲ Next to each food, write down what part of a plant it has come from. Use the list of words at the bottom of the page to help you.

rhubarb _____   beetroot _____
hazelnuts _____   beans _____
tomatoes _____   cauliflower _____
pears _____   onions _____
lettuce _____   cherries _____
celery _____   broccoli _____
peas _____   swede _____
carrots _____   cabbage _____

leaves   roots   bulbs
seeds   flowers   fruits   stems

PLANTS NEED WATER

Plants need the right amount of water for healthy growth. Making careful measurements and collecting sufficient evidence are important parts of an investigation.

†† *Whole-class investigation.*

🕐 *45–60 minutes for planning; time during 2–3 weeks for collecting evidence; 45-60 minutes for presenting findings.*

Previous skills/knowledge required

The children should understand that a plant needs specific conditions to grow well, so that it can produce food and complete its life cycle. They should be aware of the need for an investigation to be carefully planned and for a test to be fair. They should be able to measure small volumes of water.

Key background information

All plants need water for germination and growth, but different types of plant need different amounts: wetland plants require amounts of water which would cause heathland plants to rot. Many plants have strategies for surviving periods of drought, perhaps existing only as an underground root system or as hard-coated seeds.

An investigation provides relevant evidence only if the test is carried out in a scientific manner, with careful observations and measurements. When investigating with plants, it is important to use a number of specimens in order to increase the validity of the results.

Preparation

Four small trays of seedlings are needed for this investigation. For younger children, it may be better to germinate the seeds away from the classroom so that they do not confuse germination with growth. Germinate the seeds (mustard, cress, radish, grain or dried peas) a week or two earlier (depending on the growing conditions). Measure the number of seeds used for each tray carefully by counting, weighing or using spoonsful. Spread them evenly on saturated absorbent material in identical shallow containers, and cover the containers with cling film. Keep all trays under identical conditions. Water the seeds as

necessary. When the batches of seedlings are growing strongly, they can be used for the investigation. Make copies of photocopiable page 100 as needed (see below).

Resources needed

Quick-growing seeds (see above), four identical shallow containers (such as discarded food containers), cling film, containers for measuring small volumes of water, rulers or tape measures, a camera (optional); paper, writing materials; photocopiable page 100.

Vocabulary

Plants, seedlings, water, growth, healthy, amount, compare, comparisons.

What to do

This activity provides an opportunity to guide the children through the stages of an investigation.

Planning

Explain to the class that you want to find out how well young plants grow when they are given different amounts of water. Show them the trays of seedlings and ask for ideas as to how an investigation could be carried out which would help a gardener or farmer to produce the best possible crop. Discuss why it is important to use many plants when testing, not just one.

With the children, decide how much water each tray of seedlings will be given. This will depend on the size of the trays and the number of seedlings, but could be: no water, 10cm³, 20cm³, 40cm³. Watering can take place on two or three days in each week.

Ask the children what they will be looking for, what evidence they will need to collect and how the observations and measurements will be recorded. Encourage them to describe exactly how they will take measurements, and stress the need for consistency. Emphasize the importance of a fair test: ask what will be kept the same throughout the test (the trays of seedlings, the position of the trays and their handling, the way observations and measurements are taken). Make sure the children understand that the only thing that will be changed (the **variable**) is the amount of water given to each batch of seedlings.

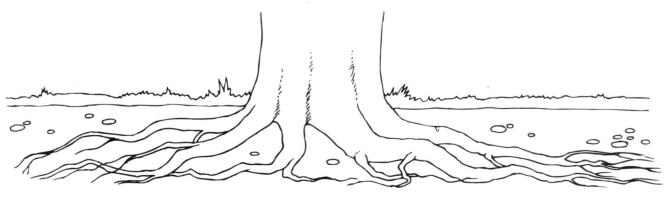

Figure 9	Observations and measurements		
	Week 1	Week 2	Week 3
Tray 1: no water			
Tray 2: 10 cm³			
Tray 3: 20 cm³			

Encourage the children to make their predictions individually, using their knowledge and experience of plant growth.

Give out copies of photocopiable page 100 (copies could be shared), which provides a structure and questions to guide the children through the recording of their plan. Devise a chart for each child to use when recording observations and measurements (Figure 9 shows an example).

Obtaining evidence
Try to let all the children take a turn at measuring and applying the amounts of water and measuring the growth of the plants. Emphasize that the test must be kept fair, the measurements recorded accurately and detailed observations of the overall condition of the seedlings recorded. Continue collecting evidence while it is useful to do so. Photographs could be taken to show the differences in growth, but should not replace written recording for most children.

Considering evidence
The children should use their results to make comparisons, recording what they find. The measurements can be presented as a bar graph, or used to draw a line graph for each batch of seedlings. Encourage the children to look for any pattern in the results, perhaps making further predictions about how the plants might continue to grow. Ask them whether the evidence collected is sufficient to draw conclusions, and whether it matches any predictions made during planning. Lead them to suggest explanations using their scientific knowledge and understanding, and remind them why many seedlings were tested each time rather than just one plant. Refer to photocopiable page 100 for guidance throughout this stage. Display a list of relevant vocabulary (see above) to help with recording.

Suggestion(s) for extension
More able children could suggest ways of improving the test – perhaps by taking measurements in a different way, or watering the seedlings at different times.

Suggestion(s) for support
Where necessary, allow minimal recording; but after discussing the investigation with the children, add comments to their work relating to their participation and understanding.

Assessment opportunities
Focus on one area of skills – for example: can the children measure accurately and record precisely; can they make useful comparisons; do they understand why it is important to use several plants instead of just one? Alternatively, assess the children's understanding of the investigation as a whole: as they proceed with the investigation, identify those children who recognize the importance of planning, carry out the test in a scientific manner and value the results.

Opportunities for IT
The children can use appropriate software to store and retrieve their observations and measurements; to produce a bar chart or line graph; and to present their findings. Photographs of the seedlings could be taken with a digital camera and incorporated into the presentation of results.

Display ideas
A 'science noticeboard' could be set up to display the observations and measurements as they are collected.

Other aspects of the PoS covered
Introduction (Sc0) 1a, b, c, d; 2a, b; 4a, b, c. Experimental and investigative science (Sc1): all aspects.

Reference to photocopiable sheet
Photocopiable page 100 provides headings and questions to guide the children through the systematic recording of the investigation. It may be useful to limit recording by encouraging the children to focus on a particular area of the investigation, such as the questions relating to predictions or fair testing.

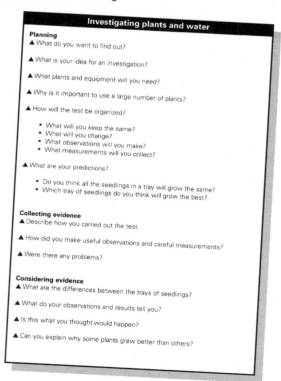

PLANTS NEED LIGHT

Green plants need a daily supply of light for healthy growth. The results of a test help us to draw conclusions.

†† *Whole-class demonstration and discussion, followed by individual recording.*

⏱ *60 minutes, plus extra time for any further tests or demonstrations.*

Previous skills/knowledge needed

The children should understand that plants need certain conditions to make their own food and grow well.

Key background information

Without light, photosynthesis cannot occur; green plants kept in the dark cannot make their own food, do not thrive and eventually die. The children can suggest ways of demonstrating or investigating the importance of light to a green plant.

Preparation

Use a piece of black polythene, held down with stones, to cover a patch of mown grass. Leave for 7–10 days. Alternatively, cover a potted plant with an opaque plastic bag (leaving the soil exposed so that watering can take place).

Resources needed

Access to an area of mown grass, or a pot plant (such as a geranium); writing and drawing materials, paper.

Vocabulary

Plant, growth, green, light, dark, cover, polythene, healthy, spindly, pale, leaves, stems.

What to do

Show the children the patch of grass which has been covered. Ask them to describe its appearance, compare it with uncovered grass, and try to explain its present condition. Make sure all the children understand that a lack of light has led to unhealthy growth.

Encourage the children to ask questions and suggest other ideas for finding out what happens to plants deprived of light. *What will happen to the grass now it is uncovered? What will happen if it is covered for a longer time, or with clear or white polythene? What will happen if a pot plant is covered with black plastic? How long will it take before anything happens to the plant? How long will it survive? Do all plants need the same amount of light? What happens to plants when the hours of daylight are shortest?* Choose one of the children's ideas and organize a test or demonstration.

Ask the children to work individually, recording what they know about plants and light by creating an illustrated information poster which uses these results. Encourage them to draw conclusions, and to make generalizations based on what they have found.

Suggestion(s) for extension

More able children could find out how market gardeners use artificial light to extend the growing seasons of plants such as tomatoes. They could research the amount of light needed by different kinds of plants to grow well (some plants need a lot of sunlight; others grow well in shady places).

Suggestion(s) for support

Children who have difficulty with recording could be given a list of relevant vocabulary, and be encouraged to map out their ideas. They can use arrows to link words and pictures, showing that plants need light to produce healthy green leaves, and that plants deprived of light produce pale, spindly leaves.

Assessment opportunities

Assess the children's scientific approach and interest from their suggestions and ideas. Focus on their ability to draw conclusions from evidence.

Opportunities for IT

The children can use word-processing software to print out appropriate words and statements for display. They can use DTP software to design information posters.

Display ideas

A large representation of the sun can be used as a background to the children's information posters.

Other aspects of the PoS covered

Introduction (Sc1) 1a, b, c, d; 2a, b; 4a, c. Experimental and investigative science 1a, b; 3b, c, d, e.

HUNDREDS OF SEEDS

A flowering plant produces hundreds of seeds, making sure that some will germinate and grow to maturity in order to continue the species.

†† *Whole-class discussion, followed by individual recording.*

🕐 *30 minutes observation and discussion; 30–45 minutes recording.*

⚠ *Warn the children that many seeds are poisonous.*

Previous skills/knowledge needed

The children should be aware that flowering plants produce seeds as part of their life cycle, and that seeds can be dispersed in a variety of ways.

Key background information

All flowering plants produce seeds when **pollination** and **fertilisation** have occurred. Some plants **disperse** their seeds more widely than others. Even when seeds are produced in great numbers, only a small percentage survive and find conditions suitable for germination. If some poppy, teasel, foxglove and honesty seeds are scattered over a school garden area, they will demonstrate the flowering plant life cycle year after year.

Preparation

Collect specimens or pictures of plants which produce vast numbers of seeds, such as poppies, teasels, honesty, willow herbs, dandelion, sycamore and oak.

Resources needed

Plant specimens or pictures (see above); reference materials describing the seed production and germination of a wide range of flowering plants; a school garden or wildlife area; hand lenses; paper, pencils.

Vocabulary

Seeds, flowering plant, germinate, reproduce, life cycle.

What to do

Give the children opportunities to examine some examples of prolific seed production (see above). If appropriate, find examples in the school grounds. Warn the children that many seeds are poisonous.

Ask the children why a plant produces seeds, and why there should be so many from just one plant. *What might happen to the seeds?* Write down all their suggestions: eaten by humans or other animals, damaged by the weather, destroyed by traffic, decomposed by micro-organisms, and so on. Point out that even when a seed does find the right conditions for germination, the new plant could be eaten by animals during its early life, never reaching maturity to bear seeds. Ask the children to draw a diagram showing what might happen to a specific seed,

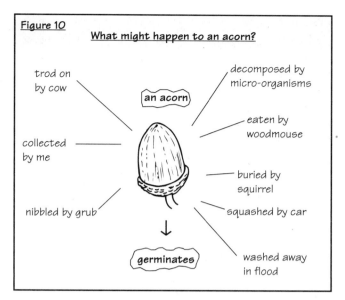

Figure 10

such as an acorn or a grain of wheat. (Figure 10 shows an example.)

Discuss the remarkable success with which some plants (such as common weeds) produce seeds and reproduce themselves; compare this with rare species which need special protection to encourage seed production and germination.

Suggestion(s) for extension

More able children could estimate how many seeds have been produced by a particular plant by multiplying the number of pods by the number of seeds in one pod. They could find out about the Seed Bank at Kew, which saves seeds from all British plants as well as those threatened with extinction in other parts of the world.

Suggestion(s) for support

Children who have difficulty with recording could be provided with an alphabetical list of vocabulary.

Assessment opportunities

Assess the children's understanding of seed dispersal as part of the life cycle of a flowering plant. Can they draw a diagram to show the sequence: pollination → fertilization → seed production → seed dispersal → germination?

Opportunities for IT

The children can compile a database of information about seeds.

Display ideas

The children could use seeds in collages, jewellery or pattern-making. They could make observational drawings of different seeds, to be displayed together with the diagrams produced in the activity.

Other aspects of the PoS covered

Introduction (Sc0) 1a, c, d; 2a, d; 4a, c; 5a, b.

THE LIFE OF A TREE

Trees, like other plants, have distinct stages and processes in their life cycle. Many species of trees are threatened by human activity.

†† *Whole-class introduction, followed by individual recording.*

⏱ *20 minutes for introduction; 60 minutes (or more) for observation and research at different times of the year, ideally autumn and spring.*

Previous skills/knowledge needed

The children should know that plants have a life cycle, and that most trees are flowering plants which produce flowers, fruits and seeds.

Key background information

Some plants (such as the dandelion) complete their life cycle within a year, and are known as **annuals**. Most trees follow the same stages, but take many years to reach maturity and produce flowers and seeds. Some trees (such as the oak, silver birch and hazel) bear the male and female flower parts separately on each tree. Conifers have a different flower structure from other types of tree. Because trees take so long to complete their life cycle, some are in danger of becoming extinct; felling and uncontrolled forest fires threaten many species. In the UK, eleven tree species are at risk, all in the Sorbus group (whitebeams and service trees); six of these have fewer than a hundred living specimens.

Preparation

Find a suitable tree, ideally a local mature tree (not a conifer) which is easy to see and safe to visit. Decide on the best times for the children to visit this tree so that they can see the flowers, and later the dispersing seeds. Devise and copy two suitable recording sheets (see Figure 11). If appropriate, arrange a visit to a tree nursery or woodland to look at young trees.

Resources needed

Pictures showing different stages in the life of a tree; other research materials relating to the flowers, fruits and seeds of familiar trees; hand lenses; 'spring' and 'autumn' recording sheets (see above), pens and pencils.

Figure 11

My tree in spring	My tree in autumn
Type of tree: Location: Observations: Describe and draw the flowers. How do you think the flowers are pollinated? Research (extra information you have found out)	Type of tree: Location: Observations: Describe and draw the fruit. How do you think the seeds are dispersed? Research (extra information you have found out)

Vocabulary

Plants, trees, life cycle, flowers, seeds, pollination, fertilization, disperse, dispersion, germination, seedling, sapling, mature.

What to do

Ask the children about any plant life cycle they have studied and the sequence of processes involved. *How long does it take to complete the cycle?* Remind the children that trees are also plants, and must produce seeds in order to carry on the species. *How many seeds do you know which come from trees?* The children may suggest acorns, various nuts and berries, sycamore keys, horse chestnuts ('conkers'), fruit pips and fruit stones. Explain that when the seeds develop, the tree will have already produced flowers, and pollination and fertilization will have occurred. The flowers of some trees (such as cherry blossom) are easily noticed; others bear inconspicuous green flowers.

Focus on a familiar tree (not a conifer) – if possible, one that the children can visit regularly. Encourage them to find out as much as possible about the life of this tree. *Is it a mature (adult) tree? If so, at what times of the year does it have flowers and fruit? If it is a young tree, what will the flowers and fruit be like? How are the flowers pollinated? Are there clues as to how the seeds are dispersed? What might happen to the seeds? Is there evidence nearby of seedlings germinating? What would happen if none of the seeds were able to germinate? Why is it important for a tree to complete its life cycle?*

Figure 12

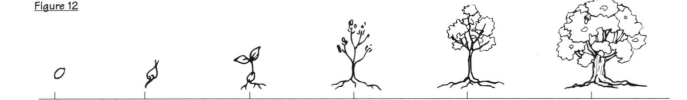

| seed | seed germinating | seedling | sapling | young tree | mature tree |

Provide copies of appropriate recording sheets. Encourage the children to record detailed observations at appropriate times of the year. They should complete their profile of the tree by researching relevant information. If appropriate, they can help a species of tree to continue by planting some tree seeds in pots. When the seedlings are thriving, they should be planted out in hedgerows, along a boundary but away from buildings.

Suggestion(s) for extension
More able children could work individually, choosing another tree (perhaps close to their home) and making observations and comparisons throughout the year.

Suggestion(s) for support
Guide less able children towards suitable reference material; or prepare an information page about the tree which is being studied, from which they can access the information they need.

Assessment opportunities
Look for the ability to produce an appropriate piece of work combining direct observation and research.

Opportunities for IT
The children can compile a database for a single tree, or collect and store information to compare the flowers, means of pollination, seed structure and seed dispersal of several trees.

Display ideas
Several children could work together to create a time line, showing the stages in the life of a tree from germination to seedling, sapling, mature tree and new seed. (See Figure 12.) This can be displayed with the children's tree profiles.

Other aspects of the PoS covered
Introduction (ScO) 1a, b, c, d; 2a, d; 4a, c; 5a, b.

A VARIED DIET

To stay healthy, we need an adequate and varied diet. We can choose what to eat in order to be healthy.

†† *Whole-class discussion, followed by individual and paired work.*

⏱ *20–30 minutes for discussion; 30–45 minutes for recording.*

Previous skills/knowledge needed
The children should understand that humans need food and water to stay alive, and that there is a wide range of foods that we can choose to eat.

Key background information
Surveys show that the diets of many British children are high in fat, sugar and salt, and are lacking in minerals and vitamins necessary for healthy growth and development. Even when children learn that a balanced diet is important, they tend to go on consuming large quantities of unsuitable food and sugary drinks. Children need encouragement and guidance to acquire sensible eating habits.

Preparation
Collect leaflets about diet and nutrition. If possible, arrange for a nutritionist to talk to the children. Cut pictures of foods from magazines to represent the main food types (see 'What to do'). Collect packets and labels representing various packaged foods (see 'Suggestion(s) for extension').

Resources needed
Five large sheets of paper or card; pictures of foods (see above); a collection of packets and labels (see above); paper, pencils.

Vocabulary
Food, diet, balanced, varied, healthy.

What to do
Encourage the children to tell you why food and water are vital to humans. Make sure they know that food is necessary for growth, to keep the body in good working order, and to provide energy for physical and mental activity. Show the children the pictures of different foods. Discuss how different types of food are essential (be sensitive to any cultural, religious and health requirements children may have):
▲ **protein** in meat, fish, eggs, cheese and pulses is needed for growth;
▲ **carbohydrate** in bread, pasta, rice and sugar is needed for energy;
▲ **fibre** in bread and vegetables is needed for digestion;
▲ **vitamins** in fruits and other foods are needed for general health.

Explain that we need a variety of different foods each day to provide us with a balanced diet (the word **diet** refers to what we regularly eat).

Ask the children to contribute to a list of foods and drinks they would like to find in their lunchboxes. Add a few (healthy) suggestions, such as carrot or celery sticks, diluted fruit juice, mineral water, less common fruits or seedless raisins. Talk about the list and sort it into five groups, writing the items in each group on a large sheet of paper or card and adding pictures if appropriate: 1. Sandwiches and rolls. 2. Fruits and vegetables. 3. Crisps, chocolate bars, biscuits and cakes. 4. Drinks. 5. Yoghurts and cheese. Point out that many prepared foods (including popular snack foods) contain a high proportion of sugar and/or fat, and that fizzy drinks usually contain large amounts of sugar. Ask the children to explain why it is important to avoid eating large quantities of these foods. They should be aware that sugar can cause teeth to decay, and that an excess of stored body fat affects fitness.

Suggest that the children each prepare a 'lunchbox menu' for a younger child, choosing something from each group to make sure that there is a good variety. The foods can be listed or drawn and labelled. The children can then form pairs and evaluate each other's lunchbox menus, substituting items where necessary so that a balanced meal is achieved.

Suggestion(s) for extension

More able children could examine the labels on packaged foods to find out their sugar and fat content. They could also look at the menu for school dinners to find out how the cook provides a balanced diet.

Suggestion(s) for support

For children who find the activity confusing, simplify the list of foods in each group and use pictures together with the food names.

Assessment opportunities

Assess how the children relate their knowledge of different types of food to their own health. Of those foods which they like, do they know some which are essential for healthy growth, some which should be eaten in moderation and some which are best avoided? Are they aware that a range of foods provides the ideal diet?

Display ideas

Some of the children's lunchbox menus can be displayed using lunchboxes and empty packets with models of fruits and vegetables. Devise an award system to emphasize the healthiest meals. Include an 'unbalanced' lunchbox meal of crisps, chocolate and fizzy pop.

Other aspects of the PoS covered

Introduction (Sc0) 1a, c, d; 2b, c; 4a, c.

PULSE RATES

The heart beats faster during exercise to give the muscles a greater supply of blood. Sometimes observations and measurements need to be repeated if reliable evidence is to be collected during an investigation.

†† *Whole-class discussion and instruction; testing in groups of three.*

🕐 *45–60 minutes for preliminary activity; 60–90 minutes for investigation.*

⚠ *Any physical activity should be part of a normal PE lesson, and should not involve tests of stamina.*

Previous skills/knowledge needed

The children will need to know that the **heart** is a muscular organ which pumps blood around the body; that each heartbeat produces a **pulse** in the wrist; and that the number of pulse beats per minute is the **pulse rate**, which increases with exercise. They will need to be able to locate their wrist pulse easily, and use a stop watch accurately.

Key background information

A single pulse rate measurement may be affected by a number of factors: previous activity, time of day, posture, and the method and accuracy of the measurement. A fair test (as far as possible) must be organized, and then be repeated to provide reasonably consistent results.

Preparation

Devise a large chart (similar to the one shown in Figure 13) on which to record the pulse rates of all the children; photocopy a smaller chart for each child. Prepare recording sheets for the investigation. (The children will need to write down their predictions, describe in detail how the test will be carried out and explain how they will make sure that the test is fair. When considering the evidence, they should match the results with their predictions and record their conclusions.)

Figure 13			
name	resting pulse rate	pulse rate after 10 jumps	pulse rate after 20 jumps

Resources needed

Stopwatches; squared paper for graphs, blank paper, pens and pencils; pulse rate charts and recording sheets (see above).

Vocabulary

Heart, pulse, pulse rate, pump, muscles, oxygen, exercise, measurement, accurate.

What to do

Refer briefly to previous work on the heart as a pump; remind the children about pulse rates. Allow them time to practise taking a pulse, first locating the wrist pulse correctly (their own and another child's) and then counting the pulses for one minute. (See Figure 14.) A group of three can organize themselves so that one person is the timer while the second counts the third child's pulse.

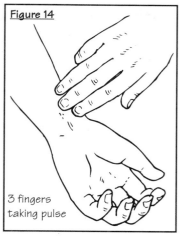

Figure 14

3 fingers taking pulse

Explain that you want to record each individual's **resting pulse rate** (after no exercise). Ask the children whether they foresee any problems. Establish that they will need several attempts before an accurate, consistent result is achieved. Let the children work in groups to record each child's resting pulse rate. Use the results to draw a large bar graph (on squared paper), which can be interpreted by asking relevant questions. *Whose was the highest/lowest pulse rate? What was the most common range for pulse rates? Are there any surprising results? How could these be explained?*

Talk about the factors which affect pulse rate. Ask the children to make a precise prediction, which can be tested, about the relationship between exercise and pulse rate – for example: *If I do ten jumps, my pulse rate will increase; if I do twenty jumps, my pulse rate will increase even more and will take even longer to get back to normal. I probably won't be able to do thirty jumps because I will get tired.* Ask them to choose one idea for testing. Can they say why it is important that all the class members are involved in the same test? Explain that if a greater number of people are tested, more evidence is available and the results are more reliable, since patterns and exceptions can be identified.

Make sure that the investigation is planned in detail and the children consider carefully how they will collect the evidence. Help them to prepare a chart on which to write their results. Their resting pulse rate, already obtained, can be recorded on this. Make sure the children understand that the exercise taken is the only factor to be changed (the **variable**), and identify the factors which must be kept the same (the **constants**): the way in which the exercise is carried out and the method of counting and timing. Encourage a scientific approach towards the method of the investigation: the children should consider their general behaviour and realize that any inefficiency on their part will affect the accuracy of the results.

Since each child's results contribute to the evidence collected, the activity need only be carried out once; however, if time and organization allow, the checking of individual results will be valuable.

Each child should draw a line graph for his or her results. These can be compared and any trends or patterns identified. Point out any result which appears to go against the main pattern, and explain how this might have led to incorrect conclusions if it were the only evidence collected in the test. The children should decide whether their original prediction matches the results, and record their conclusions. Encourage them to explain how exercise makes the heart beat faster, so that a greater supply of blood can carry oxygen to the muscles.

Suggestion(s) for extension

More able children could interpret data from other children's previous investigations into the effects of different forms of exercise on pulse rate.

Suggestion(s) for support

Some children may need step-by-step guidance through the investigation. Make sure that they complete each step before moving on.

Assessment opportunities

Focus on one aspect of the investigation, such as presenting and interpreting results: assess the children's ability to interpret a bar graph, to draw and understand a line graph, and to use these when making comparisons and giving explanations.

Opportunities for IT

The children could use an appropriate data handling package to collect and store data and to present their results as graphs.

Display ideas

The children's graphs can be displayed around a large chart of the results, with bold captions explaining how the results were obtained.

Other aspects of the PoS covered

Introduction (Sc0) 1a, b, c, d; 2 a, c; 4a, b, c; 5a, b. Experimental and investigative science (Sc1): all aspects.

SKELETONS

Many animals (including humans) have bony skeletons inside their bodies. Making comparisons helps us to understand how animals move.

♯♯ *Whole-class discussion, followed by individual work.*

🕐 *60 minutes.*

Previous skills/knowledge needed

The children need to be aware that the human skeleton is made up of many bones, supports the body and helps the muscles to control movement.

Key background information

Vertebrates are animals with an internal skeleton of bones. Mammals, birds, fish, reptiles and amphibians are all vertebrates. Animals without an internal skeleton are **invertebrates**, and include insects, worms and molluscs.

Preparation

Collect pictures and models of the human skeleton, and of vertebrate animals and their skeletons. Make one copy per child of photocopiable page 101.

Resources needed

Skeleton pictures and models (see above); photocopiable page 101.

Vocabulary

Skeleton, bones, skull, backbone, spine, mammal, bird, fish, reptile, amphibian.

What to do

Find out what the children know about their own skeletons. Can they point to their skull and jawbone, ribs and backbone? Ask them which other animals have bones. With a model or picture of the human skeleton to refer to, show the children pictures of vertebrate animals and ask them what they think these animals' skeletons might be like. *How will they differ from a human skeleton?* (Size, posture, shape of skull.) *Will there be any features common to all skeletons?* (A backbone, a skull, a jaw.) *Which skeletons will not have leg bones?* (Fishes, snakes.) *Which animal has more bones in the spine than a human?* (A snake.) *How will the skull of a dog differ from that of a human?* (The human skull is flat-faced, whereas the dog skull has a pointed face.)

Give each child a copy of photocopiable page 101 and discuss the drawings (which are not to scale). *What clues do the skeletons give about what animals they belong to?* Point out that bones are used for movement. Encourage the children to annotate features they have spotted: *a beak, no leg bones, a very long backbone, wings*. Can they relate each animal's skeleton to the way it moves?

Suggestion(s) for extension

More able children could research the skeletons of extinct animals, and how we can tell what these animals may have looked like from their bony remains.

Suggestion(s) for support

Children who have difficulty with the photocopiable sheet could be given additional clues and a word list.

Assessment opportunities

Use the children's recording on photocopiable page 101 to assess their knowledge and understanding of how the skeleton is important for moving and supporting the body of a vertebrate animal.

Opportunities for IT

The children could use an encyclopedia CD-ROM to find out more about the skeletons of various animals.

Display ideas

Pictures of animals can be displayed alongside pictures of their skeletons, so that the children can relate body shape and movement to bone arrangement.

Other aspects of the PoS covered

Introduction (Sc0) 1a, c, d; 4a, c.

Reference to photocopiable sheet

The drawings of skeletons on photocopiable page 101 are not to scale. They can be identified by looking for clues including the body shape, the number of legs/wings/fins and the shape of the jaw. The skeletons are of a fish, a bird, a frog, a dog, a snake, a lizard, a bat and a whale.

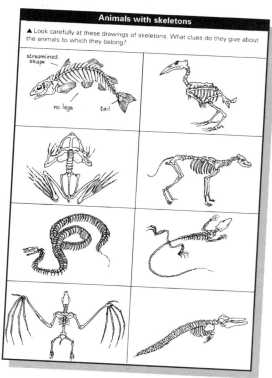

Animals with skeletons

▲ Look carefully at these drawings of skeletons. What clues do they give about the animals to which they belong?

GROWING BONES

The bones which make up the skeleton grow as the animal grows. Accurate measurement is important when carrying out an investigation.

†† *Whole-class introduction and planning; children collecting evidence in pairs and recording individually.*

⏰ *20 minutes introduction; 45–60 minutes planning; 60–90 minutes investigating and presenting results.*

▲ *Any bones used must be thoroughly cleaned and sterilized beforehand.*

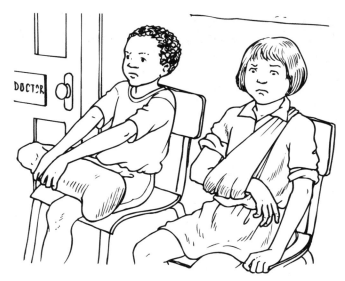

Previous skills/knowledge needed

The children should know that some animals have an internal skeleton, made up of many different bones. They should be used to find the answer to a question by carrying out an investigation.

Key background information

Scientists can discover a lot of information by examining bones. Because of previous scientific work, it is possible for bones that have been recovered from archaeological excavations not only to be identified as human, but to be distinguished as coming from males or females of a specific height, build and age. It may also be possible to interpret evidence of injuries or illnesses.

Preparation

Collect pictures and other resource materials relating to bones and the human skeleton. Devise a suitable chart to organize the children's recording (see Figure 15). Make some copies of photocopiable page 102 (see 'Suggestion(s) for support'). If possible, obtain some animal bones from a butcher or a professional supplier of bones; make sure that they are thoroughly cleaned, and be aware of any religious objections the children may have to the use of such items.

Figure 15

To be measured: ....

Name	measurement in cm

Resources needed

Pictures of bones; drawings of the human skeleton at different ages; X-ray photographs of fractures (if available); examples of bones (if appropriate); tape measures; squared and blank paper, pens and pencils; photocopiable page 102.

Vocabulary

Bones, skeleton, skull, growth, length, size, differences.

What to do

Find out what the children already know about bones: their colour, texture, strength and so on. If appropriate, provide suitable bones for them to examine. Compare pictures of baby, child and adult bones, and use X-ray photographs to show bones which are broken. Talk about how bones grow; encourage the children to ask questions. Ask them how they might investigate the differences in bone size between children of various ages, or between children and adults.

Planning

Help the children to identify a question which could be investigated, perhaps relating to arm, foot or skull measurements – for example, *Do boys have longer arms than girls?* or *Do adults have bigger heads than Year 4 children?*

Encourage the children to make and record predictions, and to consider what evidence they will need to test them. Discuss in detail how the measurements will be taken, and the importance of consistent and fair methods if the results are to be of any value. Decide how many different people's measurements should be taken to give reliable results, and prepare a chart for recording.

Obtaining evidence

The children should measure as precisely as possible. Re-emphasize the importance of accuracy if the evidence collected is to be reliable.

Considering evidence

Help the children to present their results as bar graphs and use these to make comparisons and conclusions. They should decide whether the evidence supports their predictions, and try to explain what they have found out using their scientific knowledge and understanding. (They should have found that human bones grow as their bodies get bigger, until maturity is reached.)

Suggestion(s) for extension

More confident children could investigate the differences in size between the youngest children in the school, those in Year 4 and the eldest children, and display their findings as bar graphs.

Suggestion(s) for support

Less confident children could fill in copies of photocopiable page 102, using the headings to structure their recording. Guide them through the steps as necessary, according to their experience of carrying out an investigation.

Assessment opportunities

Focus on the children's ability to collect and present evidence. Do they measure accurately and consistently, showing that they value their results? Can they construct a bar graph without help?

Opportunities for IT

A suitable data handling package can be used to store and retrieve all the measurements, and to generate bar graphs.

Display ideas

Emphasize the value of the investigation by exhibiting the children's recording and bar graphs in a busy school corridor or entrance hall.

Other aspects of the PoS covered

Introduction (Sc0) 1a, b, c, d; 2a, c; 4a, b, c. Experimental and investigative science (Sc1) 1a, b, c, d; 2b; 3a, b, c, d, e.

Reference to photocopiable sheet

Photocopiable page 102 can be used with children who need support with planning and recording their investigation.

MOVING MUSCLES

Muscles are attached to the skeleton and contract to make bones move. Muscles work harder during exercise than when resting.

†† *Whole-class introduction; individual written work.*

🕐 *30 minutes for introduction; 30–45 minutes for written work; 20 minutes for physical activity (if appropriate).*

Previous skills/knowledge needed

The children should know that muscles help animals to move.

Key background information

Skeletal muscles are attached to bones. When a muscle **contracts**, it shortens and causes the bone to move. Most muscles work in opposing pairs: as one contracts during a movement, the other is relaxed.

This activity is best carried out in the context of a PE lesson.

Preparation

Collect pictures, models, videos, CD-ROMs and other reference materials which show the working of the muscles and skeleton.

Resources needed

A variety of resource materials (see above); paper, pens and pencils.

Vocabulary

Muscles, bones, skeleton, exercise, heart, pump, blood, contract, relax.

What to do

Explain to the children that muscles and bones work together during movement. Ask them: *Where are there muscles in your bodies? What do they feel like compared to bones?* Encourage them to perform some simple, slow actions and think about the muscles which are moving: bending the elbow to raise the lower arm (the muscles in the upper arm move), clenching a fist, smiling, opening the mouth. Use a video, models or pictures to demonstrate the working of muscles, pointing out that muscles usually work in pairs.

Explain that a muscle **contracts** (shortens) to cause a movement, while the muscle which is **relaxing** lengthens. The action of each muscle is reversed for the opposite movement. Talk about energetic movements such as running and swimming, and how the heart responds by pumping faster to provide the muscles with fresh oxygen in the blood.

During a PE session, refer to the muscles used in a normal physical activity. Then challenge the children to lie

on the floor, keeping completely still while relaxing all their muscles. This is easier if parts of the body in turn are stretched and then relaxed: the face, arms and hands, legs and feet.

Back in the classroom, ask the children to create an information leaflet or poster explaining how muscles are used during exercise. They should refer to the skeleton and the need for an increased blood supply during exercise. Encourage them to include sentences, labelled diagrams and perhaps a concept map (words linked with arrows to indicate a sequence).

Suggestion(s) for extension
More able children can list differences between a body at rest and a body exercising, including muscle activity, heartbeat, pulse rate, breathing and so on.

Suggestion(s) for support
Less able children could be provided with a list of relevant vocabulary, and use it to help them build a concept map.

Assessment opportunities
Use the children's work to assess their understanding of the relationship between the skeleton and muscles. Do they understand that a bone cannot move without the action of a muscle; and that during exercise, the muscles being used need an increased blood supply to keep working?

Opportunities for IT
The children could use encyclopedia CD-ROMs to find out more about muscles and movement.

Display ideas
The children's posters and leaflets can be displayed, together with pictures of people taking exercise, under the heading *Move Those Muscles!*

Other aspects of the PoS covered
Introduction (ScO) 1a, c, d; 2a, c; 4a, c; 5a, b.

GROWING AND CHANGING

Animals are born, grow, reach maturity, reproduce to continue the species, and eventually die. Humans are dependent on parental care for a relatively long time.

†† *Whole-class discussion, followed by individual work.*

🕐 *Three sessions of 60 minutes each.*

Previous skills/knowledge needed
The children need to be aware that the human life cycle has features in common with the life cycles of many other animals.

Key background information
Parental care varies between different kinds of animals: some creatures are independent from birth, growing and developing without help from their parents (caterpillars, snails, most fish, amphibians); others are reared carefully for a short time (most birds, bees, small mammals); while most humans look after their offspring at least until they reach their teens.

Children aged ten or eleven can look back and forward over ten years. Adjust the number of years for younger children. Always discuss family life sensitively, with particular consideration for children in the class who may be looked after by non-relatives or by relatives other than parents.

Preparation
Prepare a card folded into three (see Figure 17) for the presentation of each child's work. Collect some pictures of animals at various stages in their development. Ask

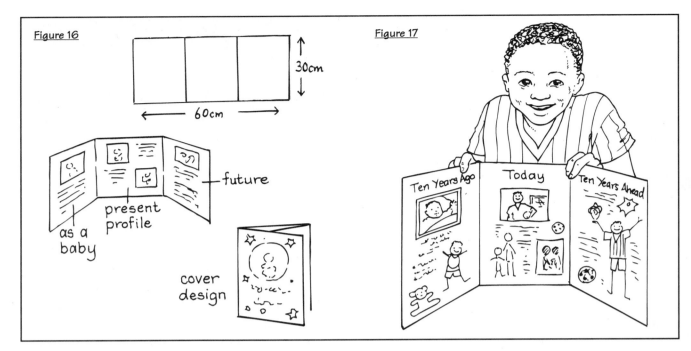

Figure 16

60cm

30cm

future

present profile

as a baby

cover design

Figure 17

Ten Years Ago   Today   Ten Years Ahead

the children to bring in photographs of themselves taken recently and when they were babies (if possible).

Resources needed
Pictures of animals (see above); one folded card per child (see above); writing and drawing materials.

What to do
Ask the children to write a profile of themselves, describing their appearance and achievements, what they like to do, who their family, carers and friends are and what possessions they treasure. They should present their work as a folded card or booklet, together with a photograph or drawing of themselves, as a record of this stage of their lives.

Next, ask the children what life was like for them ten years ago. They will need to ask questions at home, and rely on information from parents and other relations or carers. *What was I like as a baby? Did I cause a lot of trouble? What sort of care and help did I need? What food did I eat? What were mealtimes like? How did I move about? What games did I enjoy? What were my favourite toys? What are your most vivid memories of me at that time?* This research can also be presented with a photograph or drawing.

Finally, ask the children to write about what their life might be like in ten years' time. As they will probably be independent of their families, they should consider how they will organize their lives. Relate this part of the activity to the school's programme of personal, social and health education.

Encourage the children to compare their lives at these three stages and consider their development from birth to adulthood. At appropriate points throughout the activity, use pictures to talk about other animals which develop

differently – for example, calves which can stand and walk within hours of birth, puppies which can leave their mothers within months of being born.

Suggestion(s) for extension
Some children may like to research the gestation times of different mammals, perhaps talking to friends or relatives who keep pets or have reared livestock.

Suggestion(s) for support
Provide a checklist to guide less confident children through the points you want them to include.

Assessment opportunities
From their written work, assess the children's understanding of the changes which take place in their bodies to create three distinct stages of their lives.

Opportunities for IT
The children could use a word processor to present their descriptions of the three stages of their life. They could use a scanner and a DTP package to create a more sophisticated presentation with scanned-in photographs or drawings.

Display ideas
Display the children's work sensitively. Their cards or booklets can be mounted on card or paper to make a past, present and future display, as in Figure 17.

The children could also work together to create a time line showing the different stages of human growth and development.

Other aspects of the PoS covered
Introduction (Sc0) 1a, c, d; 2a, b, c; 4a, c; 5 a, b.

Materials and their properties

As their experience of and interest in the world around them grows, children need to develop a greater awareness of the uses we make of materials, our reliance on certain materials, and what we do with materials when we no longer need them. Children need to realize that their lives are affected by changes which are taking place all around them. The activities in this chapter extend children's knowledge and widen their experience of the uses of materials, and help them to explore familiar changes which occur in solids, liquids and gases. There are opportunities for direct observation, investigation and obtaining information from secondary sources.

In recognizing the range of materials around them and being aware of some of their properties, children can learn to appreciate the uses we make of them. Usually several properties are considered when choosing a material for a purpose. Children need to understand the uses we make of rocks, and their importance in creating the soils in which our food is grown.

Identifying solids, liquids and gases and comparing their characteristics helps children to understand the processes of freezing, solidifying, melting, dissolving, evaporating and condensing. They need to be aware that some processes are reversible and others are irreversible, as well as recognizing where a change of state is involved.

Where the activities involve scientific investigations, children are given opportunities to organize a fair test; to practise their skills of measuring and recording; to present their results in graphical form; to make comparisons; and to draw conclusions. The importance of communicating their findings is emphasized, as well as the importance of recognizing any risks to themselves or to others when working with materials.

By observing and investigating into materials, their properties and the processes in which they are involved, children are developing a greater awareness of the world in which we live and how our lives are influenced by the things we use and the things that happen around us. They will begin to appreciate their future role in new developments, as well as in solving potential problems.

USING MATERIALS

Materials are useful for making particular objects because of their different properties. Some properties are more important than others when deciding what material to use.

†† *Whole-class discussion, followed by individual recording.*

🕐 *60–90 minutes.*

Previous skills/knowledge needed
The children should recognize that materials have different properties, and be able to identify and group items of wood, metal, plastic, rock, paper, fabric, rubber and glass.

Key background information
Materials are chosen for particular uses according to their properties. Strength, hardness and durability are often important. Sometimes a material needs to be waterproof or absorbent, flexible or rigid. Some uses require transparent materials. Sometimes a property of a material may make it unsuitable for a particular use: it may be too heavy, liable to rust, too expensive, unsafe or in limited supply.

Sustainable resources are those which can be managed and replaced, such as wood, paper and natural fibres (all of which are provided by plants and animals). **Unsustainable resources** such as coal, oil (which is needed to make plastics), metals and rocks cannot be replaced, and will eventually be exhausted.

Preparation
Collect some objects made from different materials: wood, metal, plastic, rock, glass, paper, fabric and rubber. Include some pairs of similar objects made from different materials: bottles, buckets, bags, towels, balls, floor coverings and so on. Make one copy per child of each of photocopiable pages 103 and 104.

Resources
Items to represent a range of materials (see above); photocopiable pages 103 and 104; paper, writing materials.

Vocabulary
Materials, properties, strong, transparent, waterproof, attractive, lightweight, disposable, breakable, hard-wearing, flexible, comparison, advantages, disadvantages.

What to do
Review with the children what they know about the properties of common materials. Ask for words to describe

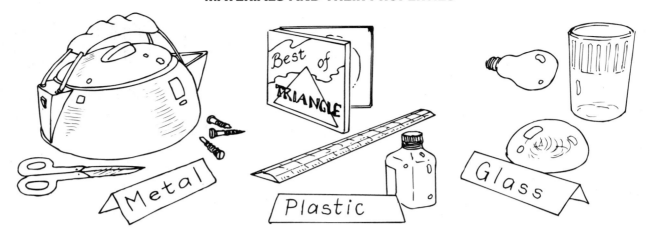

the properties of wood, metal, plastic, paper, fabric, rubber, glass and rock. If appropriate, give the children 5 to 10 minutes thinking time so that they can make quick notes; then discuss the words as a class, referring to actual examples. Encourage the children to generalize: most metals are shiny, glass usually breaks easily, wooden objects are often smooth.

Give out copies of photocopiable page 103. Ask the children to identify all the materials in the picture and say why they have been used. Elicit answers such as:

▲ **metals** for a car, a bicycle and tools because they are strong and can be moulded or hammered into shape;

▲ **glass** for windows because it is transparent: it lets in light and people can see through it;

▲ **rubber** for tyres because it is hard-wearing and flexible;

▲ **wood** for doors and fences because it is strong and attractive;

▲ **plastic** for gloves and buckets because it is waterproof and lightweight;

▲ **rock** for paving and walls because it is long-lasting and attractive;

▲ **paper** for newspapers and books because it is thin, absorbent and foldable;

▲ **fabric** for clothing and curtains because it is soft, flexible and absorbent.

The children can make their own charts (as in Figure 1) to catalogue the materials, their uses and the reasons.

Give out copies of photocopiable page 104, which shows similar objects made from different materials. Ask the children to record what the materials in each pair have in common as well as the differences, and to think about advantages and disadvantages. If possible, provide examples of some of the objects so that the children can experience properties such as weight and sound. Encourage them to consider durability, means of disposal and the possibility of recycling.

Look at some other objects which are made of different materials (see 'Preparation'). Ask the children to suggest ways of investigating which materials might be stronger, more hard-wearing, more absorbent or more flexible. A rub test using a pumice stone could indicate how hard-wearing a fabric is. The absorbency of different fabrics could be compared by measuring the volume of water remaining when a sample of the fabric has been immersed in water and then removed.

Suggestion(s) for extension
More able children could prepare an outline plan for an investigation (without actually carrying it out) to compare the properties of two materials.

They could also research sustainable materials and compare them with those which will run out. They can find out what is being done to limit the use of finite resources: recycling, choosing alternative materials and minimizing waste.

Suggestion(s) for support
Children who have difficulty in recording could be given a chart similar to Figure 1, with some words added. Provide vocabulary cards or a list of relevant words (see list above) to prompt the children and help them with spelling.

Assessment opportunities
Assess how the children apply their knowledge, experience and understanding to explain why different materials are used for different purposes.

Opportunities for IT
The children can create a database to list the properties of different materials. They can make and print labels (in a large, bold font) for display, stating the properties of materials or asking questions.

Figure 1

Material	Uses	Reasons for use
glass	house windows car windows	transparent lets light through people can see out
plastic	bucket gloves	strong lightweight waterproof

Display ideas

The children could contribute interesting objects to a display which stimulates questions and opinions about the uses of materials. For example: *Which garden trowel is best, this one with a metal blade or the one made of plastic? Which toy car would you buy, the plastic one or the wooden one? Which is easier to build with, the brick or the lump of stone?* Arrange large labels describing properties for the children to refer to when recording.

Other aspects of the PoS covered

Introduction (Sc0) 1a, b, c, d; 2a, b, d; 4a, c; 5a, b. Experimental and investigative science (Sc1) 1a.

Reference to photocopiable sheets

Photocopiable page 103 shows a scene for discussion: the children should identify as many materials as they can and relate them to their uses, then record the information on a chart. Photocopiable page 104 encourages the children to consider why similar objects might be made from different materials.

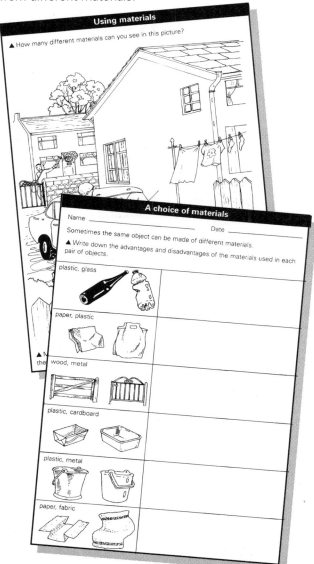

COMPARING MATERIALS

To make a fair comparison of different materials, we need to carry out an investigation.

⋔ *Whole-class investigation; individual recording.*

🕘 *20–30 minutes for initial ideas; 45–60 minutes for planning; 60–90 minutes for testing and presenting results.*

⚠ *Weights should be suspended over a large box or bin to keep feet clear. Try out the procedure beforehand and decide on the greatest mass which can be used safely.*

Previous skills/knowledge needed

The children need to have some experience of the stages of a complete investigation, and understand that the evidence obtained must be reliable. They should be able to express a question in a form that they can investigate. They should understand the difference between the words 'material' (used scientifically) and 'fabric'.

Key background information

In order to compare the properties of materials scientifically, evidence is needed which can only be obtained through an investigation. If the test conducted is fair, the evidence should be reliable. It is essential to choose a test which can be carried out safely and efficiently. Talk to the children about what is possible in the classroom, and help them to recognize any risks to themselves and others. The investigation described below tests the elasticity (stretchiness) of different fabrics. To test a different property in other materials, adapt the procedure as appropriate.

Preparation

Collect samples of similar materials which children can examine and test. If the stretchiness of fabrics is to be investigated, provide a collection of socks, tights and similar items. Make one copy per child of photocopiable page 105.

Resources

Samples of similar materials (such as fabrics); weights, coins or metal washers; hooks; thread or string; rulers or measuring tapes; photocopiable page 105; squared and plain paper, pens and pencils.

Vocabulary

Material, property, comparison, evidence, fabric, stretchy, stretchiness.

What to do

Discuss how different materials might be compared. Ask the children for ideas about how this could be done, and which materials they might want to test. Discuss the need for an investigation to provide reliable evidence, which can be used to make comparisons. Talk about testing in industrial situations, where manufacturers need precise information.

Remind the children that for an investigation in the classroom, it is important to consider safety; and that time and equipment are limited. Suggest that they try an investigation to find out which fabrics are the most stretchy – a property which is important for certain garments. Suggest that they compare different pieces of fabric, socks or tights.

Planning

Discuss how stretchiness could be measured – perhaps by adding weights to different fabrics and measuring the differences in length. Consider any problems which could arise, such as how the weights will be attached and how precise measurements will be taken. Talk about how the test can be made **fair**. The weight added is the **variable** factor. The factors to be kept **constant** include the size of the piece of fabric, how the investigation is carried out and how the measurements are taken. Encourage the children to make predictions. Help them to prepare a plan for the investigation (using photocopiable page 105 as a guide) and a chart for recording measurements.

Obtaining evidence

Encourage an efficient working method throughout the test; emphasize accurate measuring and recording. Make sure that all the children take part in adding the weights, taking the measurements and supervising each other's methods.

Considering evidence

Help the children to present their results as a bar chart, make comparisons and draw conclusions. They should check their predictions against the results and explain their results, considering the uses of the fabrics tested in the light of what they have found. Use photocopiable page 105 to guide the children through recording.

Suggestion(s) for extension

A group of more able children could be told that a new material has been developed which needs to be tested against materials already in use. Ask them how, as scientists, they would plan a test to make reliable comparisons. A new material for a chopping board, a washcloth or a waterproof bag could be considered.

Suggestion(s) for support

Children who have difficulty with recording could be given a list of key words for reference.

Assessment opportunities

Focus on the children's accuracy in measuring, recording and presenting results. Do they measure consistently? Do they use a chart correctly when writing down the measurements? Do they understand the value of the evidence collected? Can they construct a bar chart?

Opportunities for IT

The children can use an appropriate data handling program to store and retrieve the measurements, and to draw a bar chart. They can use a word processor to write planning notes and an account of the investigation for display.

Display ideas

To emphasize its importance, the investigation can be presented to others in the form of posters, scientific notes, charts and explanations.

Other aspects of the PoS covered

Introduction (Sc0) 1a, b, c, d; 2a, b, c; 4a, b, c; 5a, b. Experimental and investigative science (Sc1) 1a, b, c, d, e; 2a, b; 3a, b, c, d, e.

Reference to photocopiable page

Photocopiable page 105 is a generic planning sheet for an investigation which compares materials. The questions and headings will help the children to identify the different stages of the investigation, and can be used to guide them through their planning and recording.

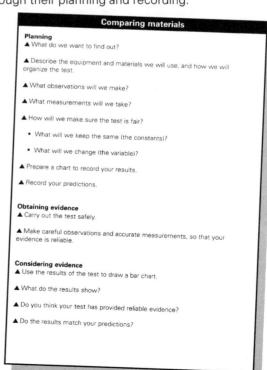

ROCKS OF THE EARTH

Rocks are used for a variety of purposes because of their characteristics. Information about rocks can be obtained from a variety of sources.

†† *Whole-class shared reading and discussion; individual recording.*

🕘 *60 minutes; extra time for further research. This activity can be adapted for the Literacy Hour.*

Previous skills/knowledge required

The children should already have examined a range of rocks, looking for similarities and differences.

Key background information

Rocks have many well-known uses; they also have important roles in food production, manufacturing processes and technology (magnetic parts, quartz in watches, silicon in computers). When discussing rock faces and quarries, remind the children of the dangers of these places.

Preparation

Collect samples of different rocks and of manufactured building materials (such as brick and concrete); pictures of natural rocky landscapes (such as mountains and cliffs); pictures of rocks in use through the ages; other appropriate reference materials. Make one copy per child of photocopiable page 106. If appropriate, arrange a visit to a safe site where rocks can be seen, such as a rock outcrop, an embankment or an outdoor activity centre.

Resources

Samples of rocks and building materials; pictures of rocks (see above); photocopiable page 106; paper, writing materials.

Vocabulary

Rock, stone, Earth, soil, mountains, cliffs, rock faces.

What to do

Display the collection of rocks and building materials. Discuss which of these come direct from the Earth, and which have been manufactured from a mixture of rock fragments and other materials.

Give out copies of photocopiable page 106 and read through the text with the class (at least twice). Ask questions about the content which the children can answer using knowledge from previous work. *Where do rocks come from? Where is the nearest place to school where natural rocks can be seen?* (A hole in the ground, a rail or road cutting, a cliff face or quarry). *Where are rocks easily seen? Where are rocks covered over?*

Figure 2		
type of rock	characteristics	uses
granite	very hard	harbour walls steps
limestone	easily cut attractive can be ground into powder	buildings making cement

Ask the children to underline the words used on the sheet to describe rocks, then make a list of their own words. Talk briefly about how rocks were formed and the constant changes which affect them. Ask the children to make a chart with the names of those rocks mentioned in the text and any others they know, the characteristics of these rocks and some examples of their uses (as in Figure 2). Refer them to the rock collection and reference materials if necessary.

Suggestion(s) for extension

More able children could research some less obvious, but important ways in which rocks influence our everyday lives – for example, in the kitchen (clay for pottery, metal for pans and cutlery, salt added to food); in the office (metal for machines, sand to make glass).

Suggestion(s) for support

Label some common rocks and write their characteristics and uses on separate cards. Less able children can match the samples to the cards, then include the information on their charts.

Assessment opportunities

Assess the children's ability to select relevant information from secondary sources.

Opportunities for IT

The children could use encyclopedia CD-ROMs to acquire further information about rocks, how they are formed and how we are dependent on them.

Display ideas

The children could create posters or information points to celebrate different rocks, describing their characteristics and uses. They can design attractive headings: *Amazing marble, Sensational slate, Lovely limestone.*

Other aspects of the PoS covered

Introduction (Sc0) 1a, c, d; 2a, b, c, d; 3b; 4a, c; 5a, b.

Reference to photocopiable sheet

Photocopiable page 106 provides some general information about rocks and their importance in human life. It can be used to promote questions and discussion. It could also be used for shared reading within the Literacy Hour, emphasizing the ways in which rocks are described (with adjectives and phrases), identifying the verbs used and discussing unfamiliar vocabulary.

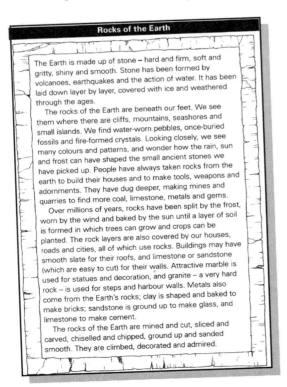

Rocks of the Earth

The Earth is made up of stone – hard and firm, soft and gritty, shiny and smooth. Stone has been formed by volcanoes, earthquakes and the action of water. It has been laid down layer by layer, covered with ice and weathered through the ages.

The rocks of the Earth are beneath our feet. We see them where there are cliffs, mountains, seashores and small islands. We find water-worn pebbles, once-buried fossils and fire-formed crystals. Looking closely, we see many colours and patterns, and wonder how the rain, sun and frost can have shaped the small ancient stones we have picked up. People have always taken rocks from the earth to build their houses and to make tools, weapons and adornments. They have dug deeper, making mines and quarries to find more coal, limestone, metals and gems.

Over millions of years, rocks have been split by the frost, worn by the wind and baked by the sun until a layer of soil is formed in which trees can grow and crops can be planted. The rock layers are also covered by our houses, roads and cities, all of which use rocks. Buildings may have smooth slate for their roofs, and limestone or sandstone (which are easy to cut) for their walls. Attractive marble is used for statues and decoration, and granite – a very hard rock – is used for steps and harbour walls. Metals also come from the Earth's rocks; clay is shaped and baked to make bricks; sandstone is ground up to make glass, and limestone to make cement.

The rocks of the Earth are mined and cut, sliced and carved, chiselled and chipped, ground up and sanded smooth. They are climbed, decorated and admired.

SIEVING SOILS

Soils consist of different kinds of particles which can be separated by sieving.

♯♯ *Whole-class introduction, followed by paired work.*

⏱ *30 minutes for introduction; 45–60 minutes for activity and recording.*

⚠ *Collect soil samples from areas where contamination from animals and pollutants is minimal. Warn children of the hazards of handling soil, including broken glass and contamination by dogs and cats. Provide disposable gloves for handling soil samples, and insist on thorough hand-washing afterwards.*

Previous skills/knowledge needed

The children should already have examined several soil samples closely, and know that **particles** are very small pieces (of anything).

Key background information

Soils are formed by the gradual wearing-down of rocks by wind, water, frost and the heat of the sun. The kind of rock from which a soil is formed determines its content. **Sandy** soils, formed by the breaking-down of sandstone rock, have relatively large individual particles; **clay** soils have small particles which stick together. Soils can also have a high **chalk** content, depending on the underlying rock. Some soils have a large number of stones; most have some **humus** (decaying plant and animal material), as well as **bacteria** and other living organisms.

Preparation

Collect samples of different soils; if possible, include sandy, clay and stony soils. Make sure the samples are dry for the activity. If needed, graded sieves can be prepared from margarine cartons by making holes from the inside with different-sized tools (such as pins and nails).

Resources needed

Soil samples (see above); a collection of sieves with different-sized holes; several wide, shallow containers for each pair of children; hand lenses; disposable gloves; reference materials relating to soils; paper, writing materials.

Vocabulary

Soil, rock, particle, component, sieve, mesh, compare, comparison.

What to do

Ask the children to remind you what differences they found when they examined soils before: appearance, colour, texture and so on. Discuss briefly how soils are formed and why they vary. Explain that different soils have different-sized particles of rock and also contain particles of other matter, such as humus. Because of the differences in particle size, it is possible to separate the components.

Ask the children to suggest ways of separating and comparing the various components of soils. Encourage them to describe their experiences of separating different-sized components – perhaps sifting lumps from flour when baking, or riddling soil when gardening. Show the children the collection of sieves and talk about the holes. *Why do some sieves have very large holes while others are made of a fine mesh? What might a particular sieve be used for?* Talk about the relationship between the size of the holes, the particles which pass through the sieve and those that are left behind.

Plan the best strategy for sieving dry soil. This could be to first use a sieve with a large mesh, through which all but the largest stones will pass; then one with a slightly smaller mesh to hold back the next largest components; followed by a further sieving with a fine mesh to hold back the smaller particles. Some children might like to use the finest mesh first and continue until only the largest stones remain. Explain that the different-sized particles obtained should be carefully collected, so that they can be examined and compared later.

Share labelled soil samples among pairs of children, so that comparisons both within and between samples can be made. Using the sieves they have chosen, the children should carefully separate the different components of their soil sample and put aside each sieving for later examination. Now encourage close observation with hand lenses, and ask the children to compare the different components they have obtained. *What do the largest particles consist of? How would you describe the smallest particles? Is there a gradual grading over your four or five sievings? Would using a different sieve have been better*

at any stage? How do the results compare with a different soil sample? Are the largest components of two different soils similar in any way? Is there any difference in size between the smallest particles of different samples? Is this due to a difference in the soils or in the method of sieving? Did you get the same result as another pair with the same type of soil? In what ways were all the soils similar? How were they different?

Bring together all the conclusions and make generalizations – for example: *Not all soils have large stones. Most soils have small pieces of plant material. The smallest particles of the clay soil are like dust. We found that the best method of sieving was... Most soils are made up of several different-sized components. We can identify and examine the components of soil by separating them, using sieves with different sizes of mesh.*

Ask the children to record the activity by writing a scientific account. They should describe what they did and what observations they made, refer to comparisons with other samples and conclude with generalizations.

Suggestion(s) for extension
More able children could experiment with different sieves to see whether the range of particles separated is any different, or try to find a way of separating the finest particles further.

Suggestion(s) for support
Children who have difficulty in structuring their activity could be given a plan to follow when sieving, and to use for reference when writing their account.

Assessment opportunities
Focus on the children's scientific approach to the activity, and their efficiency in carrying out the task. Can they work methodically? Do they make relevant observations? Can they write a scientific account, recording the steps of the exploration and concluding with the generalizations reached by the class?

Opportunities for IT
The children can use a word processor to write their account. They can produce diagrams with graphics software, perhaps using the 'autoshape' facility for the particles.

Display ideas
Samples of the components of different soils can be displayed with labels, and hand lenses provided for close observation. The children's accounts of the activity can be displayed with pictures showing the different particles (enlarged to scale).

Other aspects of the PoS covered
Introduction (Sc0) 1a, b, c, d; 2a, c; 4a, c; 5a, b.

KEEPING WARM, STAYING COOL

The materials that keep things warm can also be used to keep things cool. An investigation is important for making comparisons.

†† *Whole-class discussion, individual recording, then whole-class investigation.*

⏲ *45 minutes for initial activity; 40 minutes for planning investigation; 60–90 minutes for testing and recording.*

Previous skills/knowledge needed

The children should be aware that heat moves from a warmer area to a colder area until both are at the same temperature. They will need to have discussed and investigated materials which are used to keep things warm, and be able to read a thermometer quickly and accurately.

Key background information

This investigation should be linked with any previous investigation that the children have carried out to test which materials are best at keeping things warm. (See *Scholastic Curriculum Bank Science Key Stage Two: Materials and their properties*, page 90.) They will discover that materials used as insulation are equally effective for keeping things warm and keeping things cold: in this investigation, heat is prevented from reaching ice cubes.

Preparation

Collect the equipment and materials needed for the investigation (see below). Plan a series of questions or headings to assist the children with their planning and recording. Prepare a chart with headings as in Figure 3. Make some ice cubes.

Figure 3	
Keeping warm	**Staying cool**
Wear thick, fluffy fabrics in winter to prevent body heat escaping.	Wear lightweight thin fabrics in summer to keep the body cool.
Wrap hot take-away food in thick paper to keep the food warm.	Wrap frozen food in thick paper to prevent it from melting.
Use a vacuum flask to keep coffee hot.	Use a vacuum flask to keep iced drinks cool.
Stone walls keep rooms warm in winter by holding the heat in.	Stone walls keep rooms cool in summer by keeping the heat out.

Resources needed

Five identical containers (which could be large tins) into which plastic cups and insulating material will fit; a range of insulating materials (such as newspaper, polystyrene chips, wood shavings, plastic beads, sheep's fleece, feathers and small pieces of fabric); plastic cups; thermometers; stopwatches; ice cubes; a recording chart, writing materials.

Vocabulary

Heat, temperature, thermometer, retain, thermal insulator, insulation, melt.

What to do

Ask the children to list all the ways they can think of to keep things warm: wearing suitable clothes and adding extra layers in winter; keeping tea in a Thermos flask; wrapping take-away food in newspaper; closing doors and curtains; using special materials in buildings. Next, ask for examples of how we keep things cool: choosing light fabrics for summer clothes; using cool boxes to carry picnic food; keeping cold drinks in a Thermos flask; opening windows in rooms; building ice houses (before refrigeration was available).

Look at both lists and match comparable examples. Discuss what similarities there are, and where the same techniques or materials are used for keeping things warm and keeping things cool. The children can record the matching examples on copies of a chart (see Figure 3).

Remind the children of their previous investigation to test which materials are best for keeping things warm. *Do you think the same materials would be best for keeping things cool?* Encourage questions and ideas which can be investigated. Plan a test using ice cubes and the same materials which were tested for retaining heat. This might involve having five containers of ice: four surrounded by different insulating materials and the fifth without any insulation. Ask the children to predict the results, and to prepare a chart for recording observations and measurements. They will need to make observations at regular intervals to determine the rate at which the ice melts when insulated by each material; they should also note exactly when the ice disappears.

When the test is completed, discuss what has been found out. Ask which material was the most efficient at preventing the ice from melting – that is, at keeping the heat out. Refer to the previous investigation, where water was kept warm; ask the children whether there are any similarities or patterns in the results. Make sure that the children reach the conclusion that the same materials which keep things warm are also good at keeping things cold. Point out that these materials, which are known as **thermal insulators**, are doing the same job in each test: they are slowing down the rate at which heat is transferred, whether from hot water to the air of the classroom or from the air of the classroom to ice.

Finally, ask the children to write a paragraph explaining the usefulness of materials as thermal insulators. They should refer to the two investigations, perhaps drawing diagrams to show heat transfer (as in Figure 4).

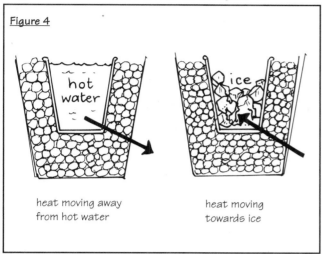

Figure 4

heat moving away from hot water

heat moving towards ice

Suggestion(s) for extension

More able children could use the results to produce a line graph, drawing lines in different colours on the same graph to show the rate at which each sample warmed up. They could research other examples of thermal insulation, perhaps identifying instances where the same material keeps things warm in winter and cool in summer (for example, the walls of a house).

Suggestion(s) for support

Guide less able children through the investigation, emphasizing comparisons with the previous test. They could draw a concept map for recording.

Assessment opportunities

Focus on the children's ability to make comparisons and draw conclusions from their results. Assess how well they understand the relationship between this investigation and their previous work on thermal insulation.

Opportunities for IT

The children can use data handling software to collect and store the results, and to draw graphs.

Display ideas

The insulating materials can be arranged in order of effectiveness, with appropriate labels. Examples of other thermal insulators could be added to the display. The children's recording can also be displayed, including enlarged copies of charts and graphs.

Other aspects of the PoS covered

Introduction (Sc0) 1a, b, c, d; 2a, b; 3a, b; 4a, b, c. Experimental and investigative science (Sc1) 1a, b, c, d; 2a, b; 3a, b, c, d, e.

CONDUCTING AND INSULATING

Some materials are useful as thermal insulators, others as thermal conductors. Materials (such as metals) which are good electrical conductors are often good thermal conductors.

✝✝ *Whole-class discussion, followed by individual recording.*

⏰ *20–30 minutes for discussion; 45–60 minutes recording.*

Previous skills/knowledge needed

The children should have explored and tested the insulating properties of materials, and understand that materials which are good thermal insulators are useful for keeping things cool as well as for keeping things warm (see 'Keeping warm, staying cool' on page 48). They should also know that some materials conduct electricity while others are insulators of electricity.

Key background information

This activity links previous work on thermal insulation/conduction and electrical insulation/conduction, making connections which might otherwise be overlooked – for example, that metals are good conductors of both heat and electricity.

Preparation

Make a collection of thermal insulating materials (and objects made with them): building materials such as wood, polystyrene, plastic, bricks and blocks; fabrics used for clothing, curtains and carpets; packaging materials such as corrugated card, bubble wrap, sponge and foam; clean feathers and fleece; food containers; wooden and plastic spoons. Collect some examples of thermal conducting materials: pieces of metal; steel and copper pans.

Resources needed

Samples of thermal insulating and conducting materials (see above); reference sources dealing with heat and electricity.

Vocabulary

Conduct, conduction, conductor, insulate, insulation, insulator, heat, thermal, electrical.

What to do

Ask the children what materials are used for their thermal insulating properties. Encourage them to look around the classroom for their first ideas. They might suggest building materials, fabrics and plastics; then think of animal fur, hair and feathers. Now ask them what materials allow heat to travel through them and are therefore used as thermal conductors.

Remind the children of their previous work on materials which conduct electricity. Ask them to think of materials which are good electrical conductors as well as being good thermal conductors. They should be able to tell you that **metals** are good both at conducting electricity and at conducting heat.

Ask the children to devise a poster or leaflet which advertises the insulating or conducting properties of a material (both thermal and electrical). They can choose one of the following, relating properties to uses:

▲ metals – thermal and electrical conductors, used for wires, pipes, kitchen tools, radiators;

▲ wood – thermal insulation in buildings;

▲ plastic – thermal insulation in buildings and pan handles, electrical insulation for wires and plugs;

▲ polystyrene – thermal insulation in packaging to keep out heat or cold;

▲ hair and feathers – thermal insulation for animals.

Make sure that a range of materials is covered within the class so that a display can be assembled and discussed, emphasizing the range of conducting and insulating materials available.

Suggestion(s) for extension

More able children could invent and advertise a new building product based on a known insulation material (such as feathers or sawdust), showing how it can be used to keep the interior of a building warm or cool.

Suggestion(s) for support

Less able children could be given a vocabulary list. Check that they have the appropriate information to hand when they are designing their poster.

Assessment opportunities

Assess how well the children can link different areas of their experience and relate their science work to a wider context.

Opportunities for IT

The children can use a DTP package to create posters and leaflets, including illustrations made using graphics software or clip art.

Display ideas

Display a variety of insulating materials (used both for keeping warm and for staying cool) so that the children can examine them; or display a collection of metals with information describing their properties as thermal and electrical conductors. Emphasize the importance of accurate information and careful presentation when selecting children's posters and leaflets for display.

Other aspects of the PoS covered

Introduction (Sc0) 1a, c, d; 2a, b, c; 4a.

SOLIDS OR LIQUIDS?

There are differences between solids and liquids; however, solids which consist of small particles flow like liquids.

✝✝ *Whole-class discussion; paired or whole-class exploration; individual recording.*

🕐 *60 minutes.*

Previous skills/knowledge needed

The children need to know what solids and liquids are.

Key background information

As their knowledge and experience of materials increases, the children will learn to make generalizations while being aware that some materials cannot easily be categorized. In describing the characteristics of solids and liquids, it is important to use words such as 'most' and 'some'. Generally, solids keep their shape and are easily controlled; liquids have no shape of their own, take on the shape of whatever is containing them, find their own level and can be poured.

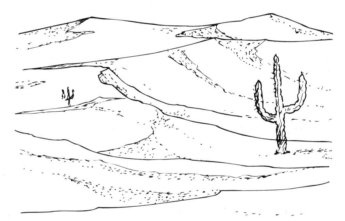

Preparation

Collect a variety of materials: solid objects such as a book, a plastic block, a key, a bottle; liquids such as water, fruit juice, vinegar, cooking oil; and solids which consist of many small particles, such as flour, sugar, rice and sand. Find a range of different-shaped containers and sieves; a water wheel toy; and pictures of large solid objects (a rock, a huge container, metal girders) and unsafe liquids (petrol, molten metal). Make one copy per child of photocopiable page 107.

Resources

Materials, equipment and pictures as listed above; photocopiable page 107.

What to do

Display a range of solids and liquids (see above) and ask the children to sort them into two groups. Discuss the reasons for the groupings. *What properties do the solids*

have in common? What is similar about the liquids? What are the differences between the solids and the liquids? Write out the children's suggestions; they will recognize that solids have a definite shape which does not usually change when the object is moved, and that liquids take on the shape of the container they are in and can be poured.

Now introduce the small-particle solids. Ask the children whether these materials are solids or liquids, referring to the generalizations made earlier. Give the children opportunities to discover how sand and rice behave like liquids by pouring them, spilling them, putting them into different-shaped containers, tilting the containers, turning a water wheel with them and sieving them.

Ask the children what they think makes these solids behave like liquids. Encourage them to recognize that the individual solid particles are very small, and that hundreds of these small separate particles together take on some features of a liquid. Handling these solids presents similar practical problems to those we have when handling liquids. Ask the children to record their observations and ideas on a copy of photocopiable page 107.

Suggestion(s) for extension

More able children could collect and examine solids such as sponge, foam rubber and cotton wool, and decide how the air contained within the solid affects the behaviour of the material.

Suggestion(s) for support

If some children are confused by the idea of solids behaving like liquids, talk to them about the properties of solids and liquids during their practical work. Assist them with their recording by providing a vocabulary list.

Assessment opportunities

Talk to the children when they are handling different solids, and use their recording on the photocopiable sheet to assess their understanding of the characteristics of solids and liquids. Do they know the differences between solids and liquids? Can they identify solids which behave like liquids?

Opportunities for IT

The children can create a database of solids and liquids, including a system for sorting different materials by means of questions.

Display ideas

Pictures and specimens of a range of solids and liquids can be displayed with appropriate labels on a table, underneath the children's statements explaining the characteristics of solids and liquids.

Other aspects of the PoS covered

Introduction (Sc0) 1a, b, c, d; 2a; 4a, c.

Reference to photocopiable sheet

Photocopiable page 107 asks the children to decide whether various items are solid or liquid; then to consider their characteristics; and finally to decide which of them are solids behaving like liquids.

Solids or liquids?

Name _____ Date _____

▲ Decide whether these items are solids or liquids. Then use ticks to show whether they behave as solids or liquids normally do.

Item	Solid or liquid?	Does it have a definite shape?	Can it be poured?	Is it easy to hold?	Does it need a container to hold it?
a chair					
vinegar					
a newspaper					
sand					
a plant pot					
soil					
beads					
fruit juice					
talcum powder					
salt					
petrol					
a ruler					

▲ Sort the items:

solids	solids behaving like liquids	liquids

SOLIDS TO LIQUIDS; LIQUIDS TO SOLIDS

Solids can change to liquids as the temperature rises; this is called melting. Liquids can become solids as the temperature falls; this is called solidifying or freezing. Both processes are reversible.

†† *Whole-class discussion; individual recording.*

🕐 *30–45 minutes class discussion (including video if available); 30–40 minutes for recording.*

Previous skills/knowledge needed

The children should be able to identify a material as being in a liquid or solid state.

Key background information

Chocolate and wax are familiar materials which exist in a solid state at normal temperatures, but need only a relatively small rise in temperature to change to a liquid state (to **melt**). Metals usually require extremely high temperatures to become **molten**, though melting metal can be demonstrated using a soldering kit. Liquids change to solids (**solidify**) if the temperature falls below a certain point; when this happens at a low temperature, it is called **freezing**. Molten **lava** from the Earth's interior solidifies when it meets cooler temperatures above the surface. The processes of melting and solidifying are reversible: solid changes to liquid and back to solid. No new material is made, though the appearance and shape of the material may have changed if it has melted and then solidified again.

Preparation

Obtain some reference sources relating to melting and freezing and the uses made of these processes; if possible, obtain a video showing metal being forged or molten lava erupting from the Earth's surface. Find examples of moulded, hammered and welded metal objects; and some solidified lava (such as pumice) from a rock collection. Make one copy per child of photocopiable page 108.

Resources needed

Reference sources and examples of materials (see above); photocopiable page 108, writing materials.

Vocabulary

Melting, freezing, molten, frozen, solid, solidify, temperature, moulding, reverse, reversible, metal, lava, wax.

What to do

Start with a short oral quiz, naming materials and asking the children to say whether each is a solid or a liquid. Go on from simple examples (such as a book, vinegar, orange juice or a key) to less straightforward examples which will promote discussion (such as an orange, some custard or a jelly). The children should realize that an orange has solid and liquid parts, and that custard and jelly can be liquid but become solid as they set.

Ask for examples of materials which change from solids to liquids; the children should suggest chocolate and wax. Ask: *Can you describe the changes?* They should use the word *melting*. If appropriate, light a candle and put some chocolate in a dish near a radiator or in sunlight, so that the children can see the processes of melting and solidifying. Check that they understand that a rise in temperature is necessary for melting to take place.

Ask the children whether they know of any materials which need extremely high temperatures for melting to occur. If possible, use pictures or a video to show molten metals and lava. Talk about what happens as the temperature cools: the materials become solid again, though their shape will have changed. Discuss the industrial processes used to reshape metals into cars, nails, keys, coins and jewellery. Explain that melting and solidifying are reversible changes. Talk about how water freezes, becoming ice, at a relatively low temperature.

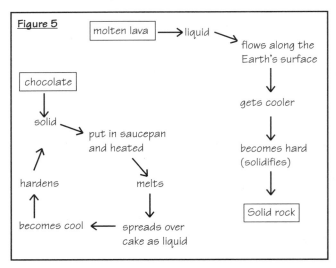

Figure 5

Ask the children to draw concept maps showing how different materials change from a liquid to a solid state or vice versa. (Figure 5 shows two examples.) Give out copies of photocopiable page 108. For each picture, the children should identify the state, the process and the temperature change (as in the first example), then give some real-life examples of the process with that material.

Suggestion(s) for extension

More confident children could research the melting points of various metals and rank them in order, starting with the one which melts most easily. They could present their findings on a temperature scale.

Suggestion(s) for support

Less confident children could be given a vocabulary list to refer to when recording.

Figure 6		
metal solid	Metals become liquid at very high temperatures.	1. Gold is melted to make coins and jewellery. 2. Aluminium cans are melted down and formed into sheets of metal for making new cans.

Assessment opportunities

The children's concept maps can be used to assess their understanding of how materials change from a liquid to a solid state and vice versa.

Opportunities for IT

The children can use encyclopedia CD-ROMs to find information about metals in industry and how lava changes from a liquid to a solid.

Display ideas

Make a table display of relevant information, children's work, metal objects and pieces of volcanic rock. Use large labels to display key words.

Other aspects of the PoS covered

Introduction 1a, c, d; 2a, b; 4a, c.

Reference to photocopiable sheet

Photocopiable page 108 provides examples of changes from liquid to solid and vice versa. In the first blank column, the children can record the process and whether a rise or a fall in temperature is required. The second blank column provides space for examples of the process. Figure 6 shows a possible answer for one of the pictures.

Solids to liquids; liquids to solids

Name _____ Date _____

Solid or liquid?	Process and temperature change	Examples
chocolate solid	melts as the temperature rises	
wax		
water		
metal		
molten lava		

AIR ALL AROUND

Air is a mixture of gases; it is all around us, and has weight. Making careful observations and repeating them helps in finding an explanation.

†† *Whole-class introduction, then paired activity and individual recording; possible further investigation (see extension activity).*

⏱ *60 minutes; more time for investigation (optional).*

⚠ *See the safety note on collecting and handling soil (page 46).*

Previous skills/knowledge needed

The children need to be aware that solids, liquids and gases exist and are different in important ways.

Key background information

Air consists of a mixture of different gases: nitrogen 78%, oxygen 21%, carbon dixoide 0.03% and other rare gases 0.97%. It is all around us, and is essential to all living organisms. Like all gases, air can get into tiny spaces. The air contained in holes in some materials can be released by squeezing them under water. Air can be compressed into tyres, inflatable toys and balloons; compressed air is **denser** than the air outside the container. **Helium**, a gas which is 'lighter' (**less dense**) than air, is used to fill balloons which will rise through the air.

Preparation

Collect the materials and equipment listed below. Make one copy per child of photocopiable page 109.

Resources needed

Four small containers and a jug for each pair of children; small pieces of sponge; samples of sand and soil (different soil samples for extension activity); a quantity of beads or marbles; balloons or inflatable toys; a small hand pump; hand lenses; an electronic balance; photocopiable page 109, paper, writing materials.

Vocabulary

Gas, air, inflate, inflatable, spaces, sponge, soil, bubbles.

What to do

Ask the children what they know about air. Discuss where it is; whether it can be seen, touched or controlled; whether it can be moved about; what sort of containers can hold it. Point out that although air cannot usually be seen, we can see the effects of its movement – for example, when the wind moves trees or washing, or when draughts blow under doors. Explain that air is difficult to handle and control except when it is contained in balloons, pipes and so on.

Make a list of examples which demonstrate the effects of the wind. Talk about how air is used in tyres, inflatable toys, air beds and balloons. Demonstrate how air can be compressed and has weight by weighing an uninflated balloon on an electronic balance and then weighing it again when it has been inflated with air. Encourage the children to list ways in which air is useful to us.

Ask the children to work in pairs, looking at how air can move into very small spaces. Provide small samples of dry sponge, sand, small beads and soil for them to examine closely with hand lenses. They should record their observations on blank paper. Ask them how they could show that there is air within the spaces of all these objects. Suggest that they squeeze the sponge under water and observe carefully what happens. Also tell them to pour a small amount of water, quite slowly, onto the other objects and make careful observations. Encourage them to explain what is happening as bubbles appear. Help them to understand that the bubbles consist of air, which is driven out of the spaces by the water. Because air is light, it rises to the surface of the water and joins the air that is around us.

Give out copies of photocopiable page 109. Ask the children to record what they saw when experimenting with the sponge and the soil samples. Suggest that they repeat these activities to check their observations. *Did the same things happen? Did you miss anything the first time? Are you more certain of what happened now? Why is it helpful to repeat a test before trying to explain the results?*

The children can now complete the sentences at the bottom of the sheet, using the phrases in the boxes to help them.

Suggestion(s) for extension

More able children could go on to investigate air in soil. Ask them how the amounts of air in different samples of soil could be compared. They can plan and carry out a test. For example: the same volume of water can be poured onto equal volumes of different soils; after all the bubbles have disappeared, the volume of soil and water can be measured for each sample. The greater the volume measured, the less air was contained in the soil.

Suggestion(s) for support

Children who have difficulty in understanding the idea that solids may contain air could focus on the sentence completion activity (see photocopiable page 109). Talk them through the completion of each sentence, and test them using a larger set of cut-out phrases (such as those in Figure 7).

Assessment opportunities

Focus on the children's observational and recording skills. Are they prepared to look closely a second time in order to check their observations? Can they describe what they saw accurately, in detail? Do they understand the importance of careful observation and recording?

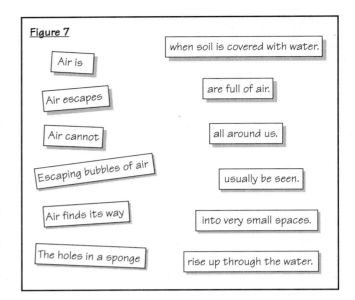

Figure 7

Air is	when soil is covered with water.
Air escapes	are full of air.
Air cannot	all around us.
Escaping bubbles of air	usually be seen.
Air finds its way	into very small spaces.
The holes in a sponge	rise up through the water.

Display ideas

Display large sentences describing air and its properties, along with appropriate pictures. Read out the sentences as a class to consolidate their knowledge.

Other aspects of the PoS covered

Introduction (Sc0) 1a, b, c, d; 2a, b; 3b; 4a, c. Experimental and investigative science (Sc1) is covered by the extension activity.

Reference to photocopiable sheet

The children can use photocopiable page 109 to record detailed observations. They can also complete the four unfinished sentences – either by writing or by cutting out, matching and sticking down the labels at the bottom of the sheet.

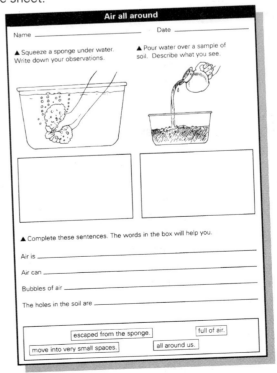

LIQUIDS TO GASES

Evaporation occurs when a liquid becomes a gas. Carrying out a fair test is the best way to obtain reliable evidence.

✝✝ *Whole-class investigation.*

🕐 *60 minutes for planning and recording; 30 minutes to set up the test; daily or hourly opportunities to collect and record observations and measurements; 45 minutes to record and present evidence.*

Previous skills/knowledge needed

The children should be aware of evaporation in everyday contexts; they should understand the need for an investigation to obtain evidence.

Key background information

When a liquid changes its state and becomes a gas, the process is known as **evaporation**. The molecules of the liquid gain energy and escape from the surface into the air. Temperature, air movement and the amount of the gas (or 'vapour') already in the air are factors which affect the rate of evaporation. Some liquids, such as petrol and perfume, evaporate more readily than water; some gases can be detected in the air by their smell.

Preparation

Following the initial planning session, collect the equipment needed and prepare suitable questions or headings to guide the children through the investigation. Make one copy per child of photocopiable page 110.

Resources needed

Several identical containers; containers with large and small openings (if appropriate); stop-clocks; pieces of fabric; rulers or measuring cylinders (as appropriate); access to suitable testing sites; photocopiable page 110.

Vocabulary

Liquid, gas, water vapour, evaporate, evaporation, rate, drying.

What to do

Discuss the children's experiences of evaporation. If necessary, remind them about wet surfaces drying after rain, washing hung up to dry, wet clothes on radiators, water spilled on floors, paintings drying, hot liquids in cooking pots losing volume, and so on. Make sure they understand that evaporation is the process of a liquid changing to a gas.

Planning

Find out what factors the children think affect the rate of evaporation. *What makes a good day for drying washing?*

Do puddles dry up more quickly when the sun is out? Discuss temperature, wind, amount of water, type of surface and area covered. Encourage the children to put their ideas and questions into a form that they can investigate. Select an appropriate question to carry out as a class investigation, such as:

▲ *Is the rate of evaporation higher in some parts of the room than in others?*

▲ *Does a wet cloth dry more quickly indoors or outdoors?*

▲ *Will water evaporate more quickly from a container with a wide opening than from one with a narrow opening?*

The children should predict what will happen and then decide what evidence they will need to collect – that is, how they will know that evaporation has taken place and how they will compare evaporation in different situations. Perhaps they will need to measure how much water has evaporated from containers in hot, warm and cool places, or from containers in sheltered and draughty spots; or how quickly pieces of cloth dry indoors and outdoors. They will also need to prepare a chart on which they can record the evidence.

Discuss how important it is for the test to be **fair** if the evidence is to be reliable. Make sure that the children understand which factor is the **variable** in the test; depending on the investigation, it could be the temperature, the place for drying or the type of container. Ask what must be kept the same. Answers may include: the amount and temperature of the water, the size and type of cloth, the type of container (unless this is the variable factor), and the way that observations and measurements are taken. Give out copies of photocopiable page 110; ask the children to record their planning on this sheet.

Obtaining evidence

As the children proceed, encourage them to consider the fairness of their test and the importance of making careful observations and accurate measurements.

Considering evidence

The children should construct graphs from their results, so that differences and trends can be seen and comparisons made. If cloth has been dried under various conditions, a timeline can be drawn and annotated to record the differences. Remind the children of their predictions: do the results bear these out? Help the children to answer the question on which they based their investigation, and to explain what they have found out using their scientific knowledge and understanding.

Suggestion(s) for extension

Children with a strong grasp of the concept of evaporation could research different methods used to dry washing, hair, skin and foods, and explain the effectiveness of some of these.

Suggestion(s) for support
Guide less confident children through the investigation step by step. Provide sentence openers or questions to guide the recording of results: *We found out that... We think that... happened because... We thought that... but... What did you find out from this test? Is this what you thought would happen? Which is the best part of the room for...? Why do you think...?*

Assessment opportunities
Focus on the children's understanding of the need for a fair test, and their scientific approach to carrying out the test as fairly and accurately as possible.

Opportunities for IT
The children could use appropriate data handling software to record their results and construct graphs.

Display ideas
Pictures showing evaporation processes can be displayed together with appropriate vocabulary. Emphasize the importance of the investigation results by displaying the children's graphs and observations.

Other aspects of the PoS covered
Introduction (Sc0) 1a, b, c, d; 2a, b; 3a, b; 4a, b, c. Experimental and investigative science (Sc1) 1a, b, c, d, e; 2a, b; 3a, b, c, d, e.

Reference to photocopiable sheet
Photocopiable page 110 provides a framework for the planning stage of the investigation, emphasizing the basic structure of the process.

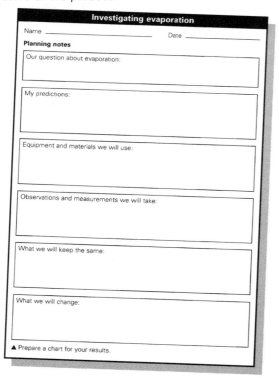

CHANGING STATE

Solid, liquid and gas are states in which materials exist. When a material changes from a solid to a liquid (for example), it has changed its state.

†† *Whole-class discussion, followed by individual recording.*

🕐 *45–60 minutes.*

Previous skills/knowledge needed
The children should be able to identify solids, liquids and gases and be aware of the processes of melting, freezing (or solidifying), evaporating and condensing.

Key background information
Evaporation and condensation are **reversible** processes, as are melting and freezing or solidifying. The rate at which water evaporates increases as the temperature rises. Different materials require different temperatures to change from a solid to a liquid state (or from a liquid back to a solid state).

Preparation
Make one copy per child of photocopiable page 111.

Resources
Photocopiable page 111; paper, writing materials; scissors and adhesive.

Vocabulary
Solid, liquid, gas, changes in state, evaporate, evaporation, condense, condensation, freeze, melt, solidify.

What to do
Remind the children that materials can be solids, liquids or gases. Explain that these are described as the **states** in which materials exist, and that sometimes we can recognize a change in the state of a material.

Discuss the scenarios in the pictures on photocopiable page 111; help the children to understand the changes involved. Identify examples where the change of state is reversed: the steam from the kettle turning to water on the cold glass; the wax of the candle melting and then solidifying. Discuss the vocabulary involved, pointing out the appropriate use of verbs and nouns (*evaporate, evaporation, evaporating* and so on).

Ask the children to write an explanation of each picture on blank paper. They should explain the processes and changes of state which are taking place by referring to changes in temperature. Check and discuss their writing; then let them cut out the pictures and explanations and stick them down on paper.

Suggestion(s) for extension
A group of children could work together to write a short

scenario which involves all of these processes and changes of state – for example, a kitchen scene, getting up in the morning or a weather story.

Suggestion(s) for support

For children who need help with photocopiable page 111, write out a simple sentence to describe each of the pictures; then cut out the pictures and sentences for each child to match up.

Assessment opportunities

Assess the children's ability to identify the processes and changes of state, as well as to explain them.

Display ideas

Display the key words prominently for reference, alongside pictures and books providing relevant information.

Other aspects of the PoS covered

Introduction (Sc0) 1a, c; 2a; 3b; 4a.

Reference to photocopiable sheet

The pictures on photocopiable page 111 illustrate different changes of state for the children to identify, describe and explain: water evaporating from wet clothes; water boiling from a kettle and steam condensing on a window; water evaporating from the sea and condensing into clouds; wax melting from a burning candle and solidifying again; a volcano erupting and lava solidifying; ice cubes melting in a drink; a wet footprint drying out; water freezing. All of these changes can be explained as due to a rise or fall in the temperature of a material.

HOW PURE IS WATER?

When a solid material dissolves in a liquid, it cannot be seen; however, it can be recovered by evaporating the liquid.

†† *Whole-class introduction, followed by paired work and individual recording.*

⏱ *60 minutes, then 45–60 minutes on the following day.*

Previous skills/knowledge needed

The children need to be aware of the process of evaporation, and understand that some solids dissolve in liquids to make a solution.

Key background information

Tap water contains natural minerals which can make water hard or soft, and small amounts of chemicals added to prevent bacterial growth. **Distilled water** is collected by **condensation**; all **impurities** are left behind as the water evaporates. Distilled water is used by scientists, doctors and engineers when water with any contamination would be harmful. Rain water can contain particles of dust and pollen collected from the atmosphere, as well as dissolved chemicals from pollution (creating **acid rain**). The quality of rain water can vary according to the wind strength and direction, the nearby industry and the time of year.

Preparation

Collect the equipment and water samples needed (see below). Make one copy per child of photocopiable page 112. Contact the local water supplier to obtain leaflets or arrange a visit to a local water treatment works; perhaps an expert may be willing to visit the school.

Resources needed

Samples of different types of water: tap water, bottled water, rain water, water from a puddle or pond, distilled water, sea or salt water, water with dissolved sugar (perhaps lemonade), water with ink or food colouring added. Identical clear containers (ideally small jars with secure lids) for samples; shallow transparent containers; hand lenses; labels; photocopiable page 112.

Vocabulary

Solid, liquid, pure, evaporate, evaporation, dissolve, solution, container, particles.

What to do

Ask the children to observe a sample of tap water closely and describe it. *Is there anything in the water, or is it completely pure?* Talk about **dissolved** materials, which are present in liquids but cannot be seen. *Can you think of a method to find out if anything is dissolved in a liquid?* If necessary, remind them about evaporation: the liquid part

Suggestion(s) for extension

Some children could collect rain water on different days, and compare the quality of the samples. Ask them what factors might affect how pure a rain sample is. They could also try evaporating the same quantities of several soft drinks to observe and compare the solids which were dissolved in them.

Suggestion(s) for support

Children who need support could be guided through the recording process, and given a vocabulary list to help with the spelling of key words.

Assessment opportunities

Assess the children's understanding of how dissolved materials can be recovered from a solution from their concept maps.

Display ideas

Arrange labelled samples of the liquids used on a table, together with the solids left after evaporation and examples of the children's recording.

Other aspects of the PoS covered

Introduction (Sc0) 1a, b, c; 2a, b; 3b; 4a, c. Experimental and investigative science (Sc1) 1b; 2b; 3b, c, e.

Reference to photocopiable sheet

Photocopiable page 112 provides a framework on which the children can record their predictions for four different samples of liquid, then note their observations and explain the results.

of a solution changes to a gas, leaving the previously dissolved material behind as a solid which can be seen. Establish that **filtering** does not remove dissolved solids.

Show the children other samples of water (see above). Tell them that **distilled water** has had all dissolved materials removed and should be completely **pure**. Point out that (apart from coloured water) the samples look the same, but may be different. Ask the children to think about which types of water are likely to contain dissolved materials, and to record their predictions for tap water and three other samples on photocopiable page 112. Put small amounts of the liquids in shallow containers, and leave them in a warm place overnight. The children can record what they did (by listing the sequence of events) if appropriate.

When all evaporation is complete, the children should use hand lenses to examine any solids left behind in the containers, recording their observations accurately on the photocopiable sheet. They can examine the containers over white and then black paper in order to see the solids more easily. Discuss the results and make comparisons: *Which type of water was the purest? Why was nothing left after the distilled water had evaporated? Were you surprised by any of the solids remaining? Would it be useful to try any of the samples again? Are any of these types of water likely to change from day to day? Will all tap water give the same results? Can you say what any of the solids might be? How do the results relate to your predictions?*

Encourage the children to show their understanding of the processes of dissolving and evaporation by drawing concept maps.

How pure is water?			
Explanations			
Observations			
Predictions			
Sample of water			
tap water			

◄ Examine each water sample carefully. Predict whether it is pure or contains dissolved materials.
◄ Evaporate the samples. Record your observations and explanations.

Name _____ Date _____

INVESTIGATING DISSOLVING

Several factors can affect the rate at which solids dissolve in water. The results of an investigation can sometimes be usefully presented as a graph.

†† *Whole-class discussion, followed by paired or small-group work.*

🕐 *60 minutes for introduction and planning; 30 minutes for testing; 60 minutes for presenting and interpreting results.*

Previous skills/knowledge needed

The children should understand that some solid materials dissolve when added to a liquid, and that together they make a solution.

Key background information

The children's previous experience of investigating will determine how independently they can carry out this activity. As far as possible, they should make their own decisions while being guided through the procedure.

Preparation

Collect the equipment and materials needed (see below). Prepare headings and questions to guide the children as necessary.

Resources

Clear containers (graduated if possible); spoons; granulated sugar, caster sugar, icing sugar and large sugar crystals; pieces of (paper) kitchen towel; jugs; stopwatches; thermometers; squared paper, pencils.

Vocabulary

Solid, liquid, dissolve, solution, stir, temperature, amount, volume, thermometer, stopwatch.

What to do

Ask the children to recall instances of dissolving they have seen, such as the way sugar dissolves in tea. Talk about ways of getting the solid to dissolve more rapidly: stirring, raising the temperature of the liquid, using more liquid, using smaller particles of the solid, and so on. Suggest that all these factors could be tested within the class, with groups or pairs of children focusing on one factor and all the results being considered at the end of the investigation.

Planning

As far as possible, allow the children to plan and organize this investigation for themselves. Make sure they all understand that they are finding out how quickly a solid dissolves, and that every test should use the same amount of solid material – for example, a level spoonful or a specific measured volume of sugar. Agree on how to decide when

dissolving is complete: when no grains of solid are visible anywhere in the water. Agree on a controlled amount of stirring – perhaps two stirs every time to start the dissolving process.

For testing the effect of temperature, the children could use very cold water from the fridge, cold tap water and hot tap water, measuring the temperature each time. For testing the effect of stirring, they could use two extra stirs, four extra, six extra and so on until dissolving is complete. For testing the effect of particle size, they could use four different kinds of white sugar (see above). For testing the effect of the volume of water, they could use a standard amount, half as much and twice as much. Discuss the fairness of the test: make sure the children understand that some constants must apply to all the tests.

If appropriate, provide the children with a list of headings and questions to guide them through the planning process:

Question: *What do you want to find out?*
Equipment: *What will you need?*
Predictions: *What do you think will happen?*
Evidence: *What will you measure?*
Fair test: *What will you keep the same? What will be changed?*

Suggest that they write their own set of detailed instructions, which they can follow when carrying out the test. A 'dry' rehearsal will help with checking whether they have everything they need, as well as with any necessary improvements to the plan. Remind the children to make a chart for collecting their results.

Collecting evidence

Only when the children are confident that their planning and organization are complete should they carry out the test. Encourage efficient working with a scientific approach to observing and recording results.

Considering evidence

Discuss the best way of presenting the results. Explain that a line graph is ideal if the temperature, number of stirs or volume of water is the factor tested, as the values of these variables can be measured. (See Figure 9.) However, a bar chart is appropriate where different types of sugar have been used. Discuss the results of the different tests: check predictions, make comparisons and provide explanations. If appropriate, provide questions or headings to help with recording.

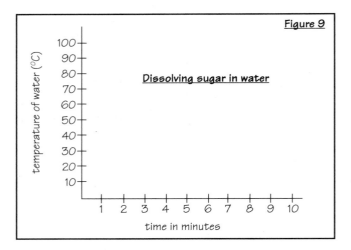

Figure 9

Suggestion(s) for extension
Ask questions to help some children make predictions by 'reading off' the line graphs: *Did the sugar take longer to dissolve with four stirs or six stirs? How long do you think it would take to dissolve with five stirs?*

Suggestion(s) for support
Some children will need close guidance throughout this investigation. Make sure that they follow the correct procedure step by step.

Assessment opportunities
Focus on the children's scientific approach: do they insist on careful measurement and methodical working (for example, stirring consistently)? Also assess their understanding of the use of graphs. Can they draw a line graph to present their results? Can they interpret results from other line graphs?

Opportunities for IT
The children can use appropriate data handling software to store, retrieve and present their results.

Display ideas
Arrange the equipment and materials, appropriately labelled, together with any necessary instructions. Display the children's results and graphs to 'announce' the results of the investigation.

Other aspects of the PoS covered
Introduction (Sc0) 1a, b, c, d; 2a; 3a, b; 4a, b, c; Experimental and investigative science (Sc1) – all aspects.

REVERSIBLE AND IRREVERSIBLE CHANGES

Materials can change. Some changes can be reversed. When new materials are made, the change is usually irreversible.

†† *Whole-class introduction, followed by individual or paired work.*

🕐 *60 minutes.*

Previous skills/knowledge needed
The children should be able to recognize solids, liquids and gases. They should have explored a range of changes, and understand the processes involved.

Key background information
This activity can be used to consolidate work on changes in materials.

Preparation
Prepare a lot of small blank pieces of card (8cm × 4cm). Make one copy per child of photocopiable page 113.

Resources
Cards (see above); pens in four different colours; photocopiable page 113.

Vocabulary
Changes, processes, evaporate, evaporation, condense, condensation, freezing, solidifying, burning, solids, liquids, gases, reversible, irreversible.

What to do
Review the changes that the children have explored in previous activities. Make sure they understand that a material may change from one state to another (for example, from liquid to gas) during a process such as evaporation.

Give each child a set of blank cards and a copy of photocopiable page 113. Ask the children to write the key words from the sheet on the cards: firstly, the names of the processes (including any different forms of the words on the same card); then, using a different colour, the words **solid**, **liquid** and **gas**; in a third colour, temperature changes; and in a fourth colour, **reversible** and **irreversible**. On other cards, they should write the names of a range of materials (such as chocolate, cement, salt, sugar, water, wood, sand and ice). They should keep a few blank cards for ideas that occur to them later.

Demonstrate how the cards can be arranged to show what happens during a variety of processes. Start with cement and water: putting these two materials (a solid and a liquid) together involves mixing, and a new solid (mortar) is produced. The change is irreversible. Show the children how to transfer the mapping to paper, using arrows to emphasize the links (as in Figure 10a).

Give the children other starting points and encourage them to create their own maps, making additional cards as necessary. Figure 10b shows an example.

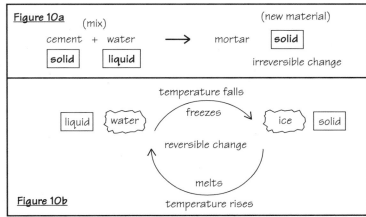

Suggestion(s) for extension
Some children could develop large maps which show several related changes – for example, to illustrate the water cycle or the preparation of a meal.

Suggestion(s) for support
If children have difficulty with mapping, select the relevant cards for a specific process and help the children to rearrange these in order to show the process.

Assessment opportunities
Assess the children's understanding of reversible and irreversible changes from their diagrams.

Display ideas
Display the children's diagrams; have cards available, so that the children can explore further arrangements.

Other aspects of the PoS covered
Introduction (Sc0) 1a, d; 2a; 3b; 4a, c.

Reference to photocopiable sheet
Photocopiable page 113 provides the vocabulary needed for the cards the children make. Read through the words, and ask the children to mark the groups of words in different colours to help them when they are making their maps.

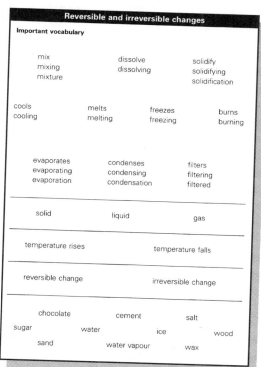

WASTE MATERIALS
Getting rid of our waste materials is a problem which we all can help to solve.
†† *Whole-class reading and discussion, followed by individual recording.*
60–90 minutes. This activity could be adapted for the Literacy Hour.

Previous skills/knowledge needed
The children should be familiar with a range of common materials and have explored their properties and uses. They should understand the everyday processes which affect solids, liquids and gases.

Vocabulary
Waste materials, rubbish, dispose, disposal, durable, biodegradable, recycling.

Key background information
Waste disposal is currently a matter of increasing concern, and sites for tipping are carefully monitored. Organic material that is densely packed and covered with soil decays slowly, producing methane gas which can be used to generate electricity. Many materials can be recycled, and local authorities need to minimize the amount of waste reaching landfill sites. Facilities exist for recycling paper, plastic, metal, garden refuse, fabrics and glass, as well as potential pollutants such as engine oil and gas from refrigerators. Certain materials can be reused directly – for example, unwanted clothing can be sent to other countries. Ideas for encouraging manufacturers and the public to create less waste (perhaps by using less packaging) should also be considered. Children should be encouraged to recognize that they can play an effective role in the management of waste disposal, both now and in the future.

Preparation
Find out about local recycling facilities, refuse disposal and landfill sites. Collect leaflets produced by the council, and

contact the County Recycling Officer. Make one copy per child of each of photocopiable pages 114 and 115.

Resources needed
Reference materials relating to waste and recycling; photocopiable pages 114 and 115.

What to do
Read together the information on photocopiable page 114. Discuss the meanings of any unfamiliar words, encouraging the children to underline these and make notes in the margins. Identify the materials mentioned, and ask the children to say which are **biodegradable**. Talk about the recycling of **durable** materials and what processes might be used. Point out that there are many unsolved problems, such as what to do with old tyres; and that the ideas of the scientists of the future – perhaps themselves! – are vitally important for all of us. Talk about local recycling initiatives and waste disposal arrangements; ask the children to suggest ways of persuading more people to recycle their rubbish.

With reference to what they have learned, the children can use photocopiable page 115 to record information about waste disposal.

Suggestion(s) for extension
A group of children could prepare a talk and demonstration to inform the rest of the school about recycling possibilities.

Suggestion(s) for support
Encourage the children to annotate the text by underlining words they are unsure of and highlighting the references to specific materials, so that they can access the information more easily.

Assessment opportunities
Consider the children's attitude toward the problem of waste, how aware they are of present and future issues, and how keen they are to provide solutions.

Opportunities for IT
The children can use a DTP package with a colour printer to create posters and leaflets. They can consider the waste disposal issues raised by the rate at which computer equipment becomes out of date.

Display ideas
The children can contribute to a large diagram which plots the destinations of common items of rubbish. (Figure 11 shows an example.) Their work on this topic can be displayed alongside official literature to emphasize its importance.

Other aspects of the PoS covered
Introduction (Sc0) 1a, c, d; 2b, c, d; 3b; 4a, c; 5a, b.

Reference to photocopiable sheets
Photocopiable page 114 provides information about waste materials; it can be used for shared reading, accessing useful facts and identifying unfamiliar vocabulary. Photocopiable page 115 provides a framework on which the children can record information about waste materials and their disposal.

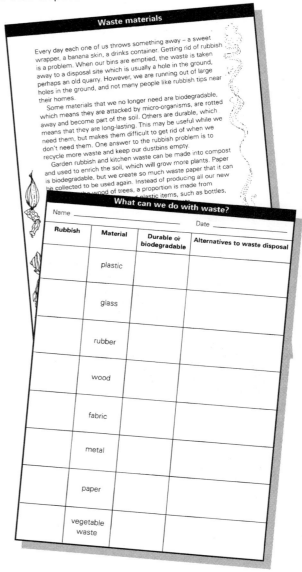

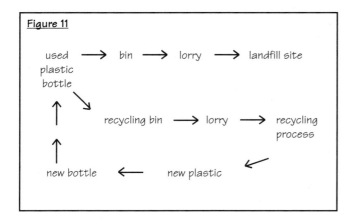

Figure 11

```
used      ──→   bin   ──→   lorry   ──→   landfill site
plastic
bottle
        ↑         ↘
        │     recycling bin  ──→  lorry  ──→  recycling
        │                                      process
        ↑
new bottle  ←──  new plastic   ←
```

Physical processes

As their interest in and experience of the world around them grows, children will want to know more about how familiar things work and to explore further the phenomena that affect their daily lives. The activities in this chapter extend the children's knowledge and widen their experience of electricity, forces, sound, light and 'the Earth and beyond'. There are opportunities for direct observation, investigation and obtaining information from secondary sources.

The children can plan and carry out investigations with simple circuits in order to enhance their understanding of electricity. Work with forces is consolidated in activities relating to magnetism, friction, springs and elastic bands, and balanced forces. The children can explore how sounds travel, and find out more (from both observation and reading) about the behaviour of shadows and the relationship of the Earth to the Sun.

In the investigation activities, the children are provided with opportunities to plan fair tests, select and use equipment, practise their skills of observing and measuring, compare results and attempt scientific explanations. The importance of communicating findings to others is emphasized, and so is the importance of safety in exploring physical processes.

Through observing, investigating and researching physical processes, the children will find themselves better equipped to make sense of the world in which they live.

THE BRIGHTNESS OF BULBS

A number of factors can affect the brightness of a bulb in a circuit. By testing one factor at a time, we can make comparisons.

†† *Whole-class introduction; paired investigation.*

🕐 *20–30 minutes introduction; 45–60 minutes planning; 60 minutes investigation and final discussion.*

⚠ *Warn the children that batteries contain hazardous chemicals, but are safe to handle if undamaged. Should any battery become damaged, it must be removed and disposed of by the teacher.*

Previous skills/knowledge needed
The children should be able to construct a simple circuit, be familiar with its components and know that a complete circuit is needed for a device to work. They should understand the need for carrying out an investigation.

Key background information
An electric current is moved around a circuit by the battery; if the **voltage** of the battery is increased, the electric **current** increases. The current is the same at any point in a simple circuit. A bulb in a circuit offers **resistance**; the fine wire of the filament becomes hot and glows, indicating the strength of the current. A second bulb added to the same circuit will reduce the flow of the current: both bulbs will glow equally, but less brightly than one bulb. The voltage of the battery and the bulb should match: a battery with a greater voltage than the bulb will initially increase its brightness, but the extra current will probably cause the bulb to burn out.

Preparation
Collect and check the equipment needed (see below). If appropriate, code the different types of bulb using different-coloured blobs of paint. Make one copy per child of photocopiable page 116.

Resources needed
Equipment for each pair of children to construct a simple circuit (a 1.5v bulb, a 1.5v battery, two leads, a bulb holder, a small screwdriver); extra 1.5v bulbs and 1.5v batteries; different (perhaps 2.5v and 3.5v) bulbs and batteries; photocopiable page 116, blank paper, writing materials; a motor (see extension activity).

Vocabulary
Circuit, battery, bulb, brighter, dimmer, match, compare, comparison.

What to do

Show the children a switched-on torch and explain that for the bulb to light, a complete electrical circuit is needed. Now show the children a complete circuit and ask them to identify each component. Discuss what is happening when the bulb lights. *How could the bulb be made brighter?* If appropriate, demonstrate using an extra battery. Explain that the bulb is now brighter but is likely to burn out, as the voltage supplied by the two batteries is greater than the voltage of the bulb. If appropriate, use two 1.5v batteries and a 1.5v bulb to demonstrate this. Discuss other changes which might affect the brightness of a bulb: adding extra bulbs, using a different-voltage battery, trying a different type of bulb and so on.

Ask the children, working in pairs, to build a circuit and carry out a systematic investigation to find out what will change the brightness of a bulb in a circuit.

Planning

Encourage the children to think carefully about changing one component at a time, and to make predictions for three changes in their circuit. They can clarify their planning by writing out their own set of instructions to follow. Provide questions and instructions to be used as a guide when planning:

▲ *What equipment will you need to make your circuit?*
▲ *Draw the circuit you will use in your investigation.*
▲ *What equipment will you need for testing? Make sure that any extra bulbs or batteries are the same type as those used in your first circuit, so that fair comparisons can be made.*
▲ *Describe exactly the order of the changes you will make in your circuit.*
▲ *Record your predictions.*
▲ *What will you look for as you carry out the tests?*
▲ *How will you record your observations?*

Photocopiable page 116 can be used to record the investigation.

Obtaining evidence

Encourage the children to work methodically, following their own instructions and using the equipment correctly. Check that they are making fair comparisons and recording accurately.

Considering evidence

When the testing is complete, discuss the results as a class. The children can write their conclusions on another sheet of paper, in the form of statements: *A bulb is brighter when... A bulb is dimmer when...*

Suggestion(s) for extension

A group of children could investigate ways of changing the speed of a motor powered by a simple circuit, and share their results with the rest of the class.

Suggestion(s) for support

Where appropriate, help children to develop a systematic method of working. Assist with writing instructions, and (if necessary) with changing a component and making and recording observations before moving on.

Assessment opportunities

Focus on the children's understanding that a fair test is necessary for useful comparisons to be made. Can the children explain how fair comparisons can be made? Ask them why it is important to change only one component at a time.

Display ideas

The equipment used in the investigation, appropriately labelled, can be shown on a table under a wall display of the children's recorded planning, observations and conclusions. Drawings of bulbs and batteries, connected with real wires, can be used to make large diagrams of the circuits tested by the children; labels can be added to state whether each bulb is bright or dim.

Other aspects of the PoS covered

Introduction (Sc0) 1a, b, c, d; 2a, b; 4a, c. Experimental and investigative science (Sc1) 1a, b, c, d, e; 2a, b; 3b, c, d.

Reference to photocopiable sheet

Photocopiable page 116 provides a framework for the children to record their intended tests and predictions during the planning stage of the investigation, and to record their observations while they are testing. The completed sheets can be used for display purposes.

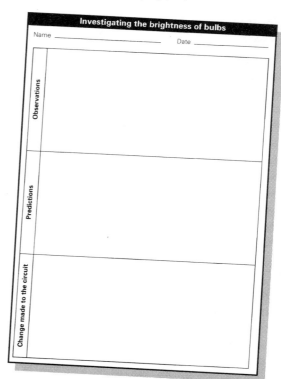

CHANGING THE WIRES

The wires used in a circuit can affect the brightness of a bulb.

†† *Whole-class introduction; small-group exploration.*

🕐 *30 minutes for introduction; 60+ minutes for exploration.*

⚠ *Remind the children of the dangers of mains electricity. Explain that using bare wires is safe in this activity, since the batteries used have a very low voltage; but exposed wires carrying mains electricity are highly dangerous and can kill a person in contact with them.*

Previous skills/knowledge needed

The children need to have chosen equipment to construct their own circuits, and understand the importance of matching the components within a circuit so that bulbs do not burn out. They should be familiar with the conventional symbols used to represent the components of a circuit, and know that some materials are better electrical conductors than others.

Key background information

Most wire used for conducting electricity is made of **copper** and covered with an insulating material. Electrical wires can also be made of steel or a mixture of metals. Thin wire introduced into a circuit increases the resistance and reduces the electric current, making a bulb dimmer. With a longer piece of thinner wire, the bulb will be dimmer still.

Preparation

Collect together and check the equipment needed. Make sure that the bulbs are of the same type and will display the same brightness, and that the batteries used by all the groups are the same. Write out a vocabulary list, and make a large poster (for reference) showing the symbols used to represent the components of a circuit.

Resources needed

Equipment for each group to construct simple circuits; wires of different types and thicknesses, including fuse wire; card; Sellotape; drawing materials; flip chart.

Vocabulary

Circuit, components, battery, bulb, wire, fuse wire, conductor, dim, bright, brighter, brightest.

What to do

Demonstrate a simple circuit and discuss the components with the children. Remind them about the importance of matching the battery with the bulb. Ask what they think will affect the brightness of a bulb. Refer to previous work on changing components. Remind the children that symbols can be used to represent a circuit in a diagram. Using the poster, ask them to help you draw the circuit you have demonstrated on the flip chart.

Show the children some different types of wire and encourage them to make comparisons. Ask: *What material are all these wires made of?* (Metal.) *Do you think there are different types of metal among these wires?* The children may recognize differences in colour and shininess. Compare differences in thickness and flexibility. *Why are some wires covered with plastic?* (Insulation for safety.)

Tell the children that the wires in a circuit can affect how bright the bulb is. Ask them to suggest ideas for changing the wire in the simple circuit. Encourage them to talk about changing the thickness, the length or the type of wire. Let the children explore their ideas, working in groups. Remind them to keep the same basic circuit design while changing the wires. Tell them that you want them to show how the brightness of a bulb is affected when the wires are changed by building three circuits to demonstrate degrees of brightness, then making comparisons using the words *bright, brighter, brightest*.

The children should draw a diagram to represent each circuit using symbols, then devise an interesting method of demonstrating their bulbs. Suggest that they prepare three star shapes to which they can attach their bulbs, concealing the rest of each circuit behind its star shape. (See Figure 1.) Alternatively, they could devise an illuminated advertisement which uses different degrees of brightness.

Provide an instruction list to which the children can refer as they work:

Show how the wire in a circuit affects the brightness of a bulb.

1. Construct three circuits, using the same type of batteries and bulbs in each.
2. Change the wires so that the bulb in each circuit shows a different brightness.
3. Arrange the three

Figure 1

circuits in order of brightness and label the bulbs *bright, brighter, brightest.*

4. Draw each circuit using symbols. Add extra information to show the changes you have made.

5. Think of an interesting way to demonstrate the brightness of the bulbs.

6. Write sentences to explain how changing the wires affects the brightness of the bulbs.

Give each group the opportunity to talk about and show their demonstrations. Help the children to make generalizations about how the brightness of the bulbs is affected by changing the wires in a circuit – for example: *The thinner the wire, the dimmer the bulb.*

Suggestion(s) for extension

Some children could try to set up circuits to make four degrees of brightness. They could also find out (by reading) about the use of a fuse as a safety device in a mains circuit.

Suggestion(s) for support

If necessary, make suggestions for the children to try, such as using a longer piece of thin wire. Encourage them to use the poster for reference when drawing their circuit diagrams.

Assessment opportunities

As the children work, assess their scientific attitude. Do they listen to each other's ideas and share the task sensibly? Use the children's drawings to assess their understanding of circuits and the use of symbols to represent components.

Display ideas

Arrange each group's demonstration, with appropriate labels and diagrams. Write out or print in bold text the conclusions which have been reached.

Other aspects of the PoS covered

Introduction (Sc0) 1a, b, c; 2a, b; 4a, c; 5a, b. Materials and their properties (Sc3) 1c.

MAGNETIC FORCES

There are forces between magnets: they can attract and repel each other. By observing carefully, we can learn about these forces.

†† *Whole-class introduction; paired practical work; whole-class discussion.*

🕒 *20 minutes introduction; 60 minutes exploring, recording and discussing.*

Previous skills/knowledge needed

The children should be aware that pushes and pulls are forces, and know that magnets exert forces.

Key background information

A magnet has two regions where the force it exerts is strongest. These are known as the (**north and south) poles**. Unlike poles attract each other; like poles repel each other. The poles may be at the ends of a magnet (as in a bar magnet) or on opposite sides (as in a ring magnet). True magnets will attract **and** repel other magnets; materials which are **magnetic** are attracted only. If there is no attraction between a magnet and a material, the material is non-magnetic.

Preparation

Collect a variety of magnets (see 'What to do'). Arrange areas around the room which the children can visit to explore different types of magnets.

Resources needed

A collection of magnets (see 'What to do'); small stickers; reference material on magnets and their uses.

Vocabulary

Magnet, magnetic, force, attract, attraction, repel, repulsion.

What to do

Encourage the children to demonstrate forces within the classroom by picking up a pencil, opening a window, pushing a book across a desk, opening a drawer and so on. Relate the movement of the object to the force applied.

Ask what the children know about forces between magnets. Tell them that magnets can pull towards (attract) each other with the force of **attraction**, and can also push away from (repel) each other with the force of **repulsion**.

Working in pairs, the children can explore the forces exerted by different magnets. They should observe carefully and record what happens in detail. Set up areas for practical work. Try to include:

▲ a very strong magnet which enables the children to feel the forces it exerts on other magnets;

▲ a range of bar magnets;

▲ a horseshoe magnet together with a bar magnet;

▲ ring magnets with a rod;

▲ a magnet in a dish which is floating on water, plus another (bar) magnet;

▲ a suspended bar magnet, plus another bar magnet;

▲ any other magnets available.

Provide small stickers which the children can use to identify different parts of a magnet. They might decide to use colours or symbols to show which parts of a magnet attract and repel other magnets. Provide a recording sheet for the children to draw and describe the magnets used and to record their observations of what happens.

Bring the children back together to discuss their findings. Ask them to describe the effects that they have observed when bringing different magnets together, including the movement of a magnet floating on water and that of a magnet suspended in air. Make sure that they are using correct vocabulary, and encourage general statements to describe the behaviour of magnets.

Suggest that the children devise a game or demonstration which uses attraction and repulsion – for example, a drawing of a dog's head fastened to one end of a bar magnet could refuse or accept different foods offered at each end of a second bar magnet. Use this opportunity to discuss the correct handling and storage of magnets: the magnetic force is weakened if magnets are dropped or heated; magnets should be stored in pairs, with unlike ends next to each other.

Suggestion(s) for extension
Children could research the uses made of the force of magnetic attraction, and relate these to work on the uses of magnetic materials.

Suggestion(s) for support
To ease children into this activity, label the ends of two bar magnets with different-coloured stickers (perhaps red and blue), and ask the children to explore and describe the forces between the magnets.

Assessment opportunities
Observe and discuss the children's practical work to assess their understanding of magnetic forces. Do they use correct vocabulary? Do they make careful observations? Assess their ability to record in a scientific way.

Display ideas
Arrange a collection of labelled magnets, together with appropriate vocabulary. Write out and display useful statements from the children's recording. Display any demonstrations or games the children have devised for others to try out.

Other aspects of the PoS covered
Introduction (Sc0) 1a, b, c; 2a, b; 4a, c. Experimental and investigative science (Sc1) 2a, b.

MEASURING FORCES

Forces can be measured; a force meter, sometimes called a newton meter, is used to measure forces.

†† *Whole-class introduction, followed by paired work.*

⏲ *20–30 minutes for introduction; 45 minutes for activity.*

Previous skills/knowledge needed
The children should understand that pushes and pulls are forces, and that the effect of a force depends on its size. They should be able to recognize a range of forces, including magnetic attraction and repulsion and the forces exerted by stretched and compressed springs.

Key background information
Force, including weight, is measured in **newtons**. A force meter, also known as a **newton meter**, is used to measure forces. This is a type of spring balance which is calibrated in newtons; some force meters measure forces up to 1 newton, others up to 5, 10, 20, 30, 50 or 100 newtons. A newton is the amount of force needed to make a mass of 1kg speed up by 1 metre per second in 1 second.

Preparation
Collect and check a variety of different force meters.

Resources needed
Force meters of various types; paper, writing materials.

Vocabulary
Forces, force meter, newton, newton meter, calibration, scale, measure, measurement.

What to do
Remind the children of the forces with which they are familiar. Compare the sizes of forces by talking about the effects of different pushes on the same object (a harder kick makes a ball travel much further) and the different pulls required to move similar-sized objects of different weights (an empty box needs a smaller pull to lift it than the same box full of marbles). Explain that there is a force between an object and a surface which prevents the object from moving, and that a greater force is needed to make the object move.

Tell the children that forces can be measured accurately with an instrument called a force meter. Let them examine force meters of various types, making comparisons. Point out the spring and discuss how the meter works. Examine the calibrations, and tell the children that forces are measured in newtons (N) – named after the scientist Sir Isaac Newton, whose scientific thinking helped to explain many ideas about forces. Ask the children what is the greatest force the force meter they have can measure, and what is the least. Suggest that they measure some forces, such as those needed to open a cupboard door or to pull various objects across a table. Working in pairs, they can use the force meter to feel a force of 1 newton, then 5, 10 and 20 newtons.

Suggest pulling an object over different surfaces, such as a table top and a carpet, and finding out what force is needed to move the object each time. If they understand the limits of the force meters, the children can avoid overstretching the spring and damaging their instrument. Make sure they understand that the higher the reading on the force meter, the greater is the force used.

The children can make a chart to record the forces they have measured. They can then list the forces they have measured in order, starting with the smallest.

Suggestion(s) for extension
Some children could prepare a demonstration for the rest of the class of the forces required to move an object over different surfaces.

Suggestion(s) for support
Individual guidance in reading the scale of the force meter will give children the confidence and motivation to move on to measuring independently.

Assessment opportunities
Assess the children's accuracy in reading the force meters. Use their recording charts to assess their understanding of what is being measured. Ask them to say which is the greatest force they have measured, and which of two measurements indicates the lesser force.

Opportunities for IT
The children can use CD-ROMs to find out about Sir Isaac Newton.

Display ideas
Display some force meters for the children to examine, and a large labelled drawing of a force meter for reference.

Other aspects of the PoS covered
Introduction (Sc0) 1a, b, c, d; 4a, b, c. Experimental and investigative science (Sc1) 2a, b.

⬙🄿 SLIDE AWAY

The size of the force required to start an object moving over different surfaces will vary. Collecting the right evidence during an investigation is important for answering a question.

✛✛ *Paired investigation; whole-class discussion to start and finish.*

🕐 *45 minutes for planning; 60 minutes for testing, recording and discussion.*

Previous skills/knowledge needed
The children should be aware of a range of forces, and know that forces differ in size and can be measured using a force meter. They need to understand that when an object slides down a slope, it does so because of gravity.

Key background information
A force applied to a stationary object may cause it to move. Other forces also acting on the object will determine the size of the force needed to start movement. Objects on a flat surface can be pulled, and the force applied measured by a force meter. Objects on a slope slide downwards due to the force of **gravity**.

Preparation
Collect the equipment and materials needed (see below). Make one copy per child of photocopiable page 117; prepare any extra questions needed to guide the children through their investigation.

Resources needed
Several pieces each of three or four differently-textured surfaces (such as carpet, wood, vinyl and non-slip floor covering); force meters; rulers (for measuring); squared paper, writing materials; photocopiable page 117; access to different floor and outdoor surfaces (see extension activity).

Vocabulary
Force, force meter, surface, evidence, constant, variable.

What to do
Tell the children that you want them to use their knowledge and experience of forces to answer the question: *Which surfaces do objects slide on most easily?* They could investigate this either by measuring the force required to start an object moving on each type of surface or by measuring the height of the slope required before an object will slide down. The object could be anything to which a force meter can be attached, such as a box of weights or a shoe filled with marbles. A slope can be increased using thin identical books (exercise books or magazines), which can be counted as a rough measure of height.

Planning

Remind the children that the investigation must help to answer their question. They should think carefully about the evidence they will collect. Allow them time to discuss the question in pairs and decide on a method of investigation. Where necessary, offer clues and advice while talking with each pair.

When the children have discussed their ideas, they should write down a plan (using photocopiable page 117). Check that they are sure how the evidence they are collecting will answer their question; and that they are aware of the importance of a fair test, and can identify the **constants** (same object, same methods of working, same way of collecting measurements) and the **variable** (different surfaces). They should prepare a chart to collect their results (as in Figure 3).

Figure 3

type of surface	height of slope	type of surface	force required to move objects
wood		wood	
carpet		carpet	
vinyl		vinyl	
plastic		plastic	

Obtaining evidence

Encourage a scientific attitude to working, as well as accurate observation, measuring and recording. Check that those children using force meters are reading the scale correctly, and that those changing the height of a slope are measuring accurately. Make sure the children understand that both types of investigation are varying the force applied to the object: making the slope steeper increases the pull of gravity on the object. Remind the children that the test must be carried out fairly, and that the **variable** is the surface used.

Considering evidence

Ask the children to present their results as a bar chart. Use these to compare the different tests and judge how effective they were at providing the evidence needed. Ask the children to explain what the force meter readings and the different slope heights indicate. Use questions to prompt their recording: *What have you found out? Is it what you thought would happen? What can you conclude from this? Why is it important to use correct surfaces for roads, footpaths and corridors?*

Suggestion(s) for extension

Some children could try measuring the forces needed to move the object on other surfaces such as different floors, mown grass or a tarmac path.

Suggestion(s) for support

Where necessary, check each step of the investigation procedure with the children. Assist with making force meter readings, and with adjusting and measuring the height of the slope.

Assessment opportunities

Focus on the children's scientific approach to the investigation. Do they work methodically and insist on accuracy? Do they check their force meter readings with each other? Do they assist each other in measuring the slope? Assess their understanding of what the evidence indicates. Can they use their results to show which surfaces make it more difficult for objects to start moving? Do they understand that the less force is required, the more easily an object can start to move?

Opportunities for IT

The children can use data handling software to construct bar charts.

Display ideas

Help the children to use the equipment and recording to arrange a demonstration showing what they have done.

Other aspects of the PoS covered

Introduction (Sc0) 1a, b, c, d; 2a, b; 4a, b, c. Experimental and investigative science (Sc1) 1a, b, c, d; 2a, b; 3a, b, c, d.

Reference to photocopiable sheet

Photocopiable page 117 provides a framework which the children can use to record the planning stage of their investigation.

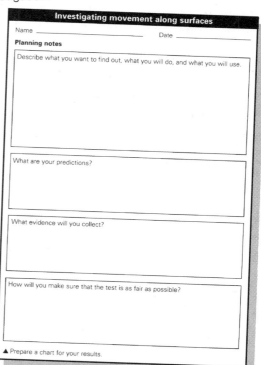

HIGH AND LOW FRICTION

Sometimes friction is useful; sometimes it needs to be overcome.

†† *Whole-class discussion, followed by individual work.*

🕑 *45–60 minutes.*

Previous skills/knowledge needed
The children need to understand that forces are pushes and pulls, and that they can speed up or slow down moving objects.

Key background information
Friction is a force which opposes the relative movement of two surfaces. An object moving along a surface will be slowed down by friction.

Preparation
Collect examples and pictures of high-friction materials (non-slip gloves and shoes, different tyre treads, textured floor coverings, grip handles) and low-friction materials and examples (skates, skis, slides, balls, vehicles skidding, machinery running). Make one copy per child of photocopiable page 118.

Resources needed
Small cubes; examples and pictures (see above); photocopiable page 118.

Vocabulary
Low friction, high friction, surface, grip, slide.

What to do
Ask the children to push a plastic cube gently, with one finger, across different surfaces such as a desk top, a piece of paper, their clothing and the floor. Explain that there is a force which is acting against this movement and slowing the object down; this force is **friction**. Ask the children whether they noticed any difference in the movement along the various surfaces. Tell them that when the cube moved easily, there was less friction; when it seemed to stick, there was more friction.

Discuss familiar examples of friction: footballs rolling over grass or tarmac; toy cars travelling over carpeted or wooden floors; shoes gripping or slipping on different surfaces. Look at examples of high and low friction materials (see above). Point out that sometimes high friction is required to stop things slipping, and sometimes low friction is required to let things slide or move easily.

Look at the examples on photocopiable page 118. Discuss the situation illustrated in each picture; ask the children to decide whether high or low friction is important, and to write an explanation. They can also describe examples of their own on the back of the sheet.

Suggestion(s) for extension
Some children could go on to compile two lists of examples: one where high friction is useful and one where low friction is useful. Ask them whether one list was easier to compile than the other.

Suggestion(s) for support
Some children could be provided with a vocabulary list to use as reference when recording.

Assessment opportunities
From the children's work on photocopiable page 118, assess their ability to relate their knowledge and understanding of friction to its uses in everyday situations. Can they recognize when friction is useful in restricting movement, and when it is important to reduce friction in order to allow movement?

Display ideas
The children's work from this activity can be combined with reference materials to create two contrasting displays: 'High friction' and 'Low friction'.

Other aspects of the PoS covered
Introduction (Sc0) 1a, c, d; 2a, b; 4a.

Reference to photocopiable sheet
Page 118 contains six pictures. For each picture, the child should decide whether high or low friction is important and write a sentence to explain the situation – for example: *High friction. The goalkeeper's gloves must grip the ball to stop it when it is moving fast through the air, and to throw it accurately.*

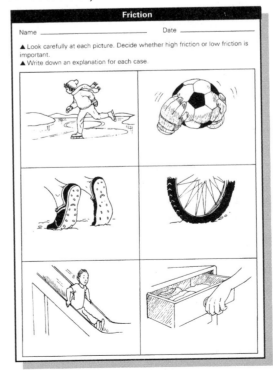

WATER RESISTANCE

An object moving through water is slowed down by the resisting force of the water. We can find out how water resistance affects objects of different shapes by carrying out an investigation.

†† *Whole-class discussion and investigation.*

🕐 *60 minutes for introduction and planning; 60 minutes for testing and concluding.*

Previous skills/knowledge needed

The children should know that friction forces act upon moving objects to slow them down.

Key background information

Water resistance, like air resistance, is a friction force: it opposes the movement of objects through water.

Preparation

Collect the equipment and materials needed (see below). Make one copy per child of photocopiable page 119.

Resources needed

A plastic bowl or tank; a large plastic ball; a tall transparent container such as a large sweet jar or glass cylinder; small items such as a paper clip, a coin and a pebble; Plasticine; a stopwatch; photocopiable page 119, writing materials; a video showing aquatic animals or boats.

Vocabulary

Force, water resistance, shape, friction.

What to do

Discuss the children's experiences of swimming or walking through water. *What happens when you try to move your feet quickly?* Explain that water provides a friction force which slows down movement; this force is called **water resistance**.

Show the class a tall transparent jar filled with water. Drop several items (such as a coin, a paperclip and a small stone) into the water; ask the children to observe carefully and comment on how the objects move. Encourage discussion about the effect of shape on water resistance. Ask for ideas about why some creatures and boats appear to move easily against the resistance of water. If possible, show a short video of aquatic animals or boats.

Refer to the tall jar and ask the children to suggest ideas for an investigation to compare the movement of different shapes through water. Tell them that you want them to use a small piece of Plasticine, changing its shape and observing its movement through the water each time.

Planning

Emphasize the importance of detailed planning before the test is begun. Take the children through the stages of the planning procedure. Start with the question to be answered: *Which shapes move most easily through water?* Then ask:

▲ *How will the test be organized?* (How much Plasticine will be used; what shapes we will test.)

▲ *What equipment is needed?* (A tall transparent jar, a piece of Plasticine, a stopwatch.)

▲ *What observations will be made?* (We will watch carefully how each shape travels through the water.)

▲ *What measurements will we take?* (We will use a stopwatch to find out how long it takes for the Plasticine to reach the bottom of the jar. We will need to start the stopwatch exactly when each shape is dropped into the water to make a fair comparison.)

▲ *How will we record our measurements and observations?* (We need a chart with spaces to write what we observe and the times measured.)

▲ *How will we make our test fair?* (We will make sure that the same amount of water is in the jar every time, the same piece of Plasticine is used, and the test is carried out in exactly the same way each time.)

▲ *What predictions will we make?* (Which shape will move most easily through the water? Which shape will take the longest time to reach the bottom?)

Suggest that the children create a strip cartoon to set out their planning, using diagrams, words and phrases.

Obtaining evidence

If necessary, remind the children of the need for a fair test and for accurate recording of observations and measurements. Ask: *How can we make sure the stopwatch is started at exactly the same time that the shape is dropped?* (Perhaps by counting down.) *How can you describe the movement of each shape through the water? Why should the plasticine be carefully dried each time?* Point out that it might be useful to repeat some parts of the test in order to check the results. *Why would it be useful to time each shape three times?* Photocopiable page 119 can be used for recording.

Considering evidence

Discuss the results with the children; help them to make comparisons, draw conclusions and check these against their predictions. Encourage explanations which refer to the resisting force of the water against the moving shapes. Ask questions to assist recording: *What have you found out from your test? Is this what you thought would happen? Why do some shapes move more easily through water than others?* The children should understand that shapes with a wider downward-facing surface meet more resistance from the water than more vertically narrow, **streamlined** shapes.

Suggestion(s) for extension

Some children could go on to write and illustrate a

description or story which includes accurate references to water resistance.

Suggestion(s) for support

Where necessary, emphasize the principles of a fair test – especially the importance of consistent methods of working, observing and measuring.

Assessment opportunities

Focus on the children's understanding of a fair test, and their ability to explain the relationship between an object's shape and its movement through water in terms of water resistance.

Opportunities for IT

The children can use a word-processor to present their results and explanations. They can use art software (including the 'spray' and 'autoshape' facilities) to create underwater scenes as part of a display.

Display ideas

Labelled pictures or photographs of various aquatic scenes can be used to show how aquatic animals and boats both take advantage of water resistance and overcome it. Display the children's plans, results and explanations.

Other aspects of the PoS covered

Introduction (Sc0) 1a, b, c, d; 2a, b; 4a, b. Experimental and investigative science (Sc1) 1b, c, d; 2b, c; 3a, b, c, d, e.

Reference to photocopiable sheet

Photocopiable page 119 can be used to record the investigation results.

Water resistance		
Name _____ Date _____		
▲ Compare the movement of different shapes through water.		
Draw and describe each shape	Observations	Time taken to reach bottom of jar

THE FORCE OF AIR

Air resistance is a force that slows objects moving through the air.

†† *Whole-class activity, then paired activity and individual recording.*

⏲ *40 minutes for whole-class activity; 30 minutes for paired activity; 45 minutes for recording.*

⚠ *Children need to be aware of the dangers of heights, and warned that dropping an object from a high point endangers people below.*

Previous skills/knowledge needed

The children need to know that friction forces act on moving objects and can slow them down.

Key background information

Air resistance, like water resistance, is a friction force: it opposes the movement of objects.

Preparation

Find pictures and reference materials to do with the force of air and the application of air resistance (bird flight, aircraft, fireworks and so on).

Resources needed

Several large pieces of card; A4 paper; sheets of foil (or large foil pie dishes); tissues or kitchen paper; pictures and reference materials (see above).

Vocabulary

Force, friction, air resistance, height.

What to do

Take the class to an open space such as the playground. In turn, give groups of children large pieces of card; ask them to run across the playground, holding the cards in front of them, while the other groups observe. Ask the children what they felt and what they observed. Encourage them to talk about the force of the air, pushing against the card and making running more difficult. Explain that the force of the air is called **air resistance** and is a friction force. Talk about what happens when the force of air resistance is increased by the movement of air (wind). What does the wind do to kites and umbrellas? Relate the surface area of an object to the force of the air: the bigger the surface area, the greater the air resistance.

Back in the classroom, give each pair of children two sheets of A4 paper, two pieces of aluminium foil and two tissues or paper towels. Ask them to scrunch one piece of each material into a tight ball, then drop both pieces of the same material at the same time and compare how they fall to the ground. Increasing the distance of fall by dropping the objects from a safe platform would be helpful; but avoid dangerous situations, and warn the children against dropping any object from a great height. The children should notice that balls of each material fall to the ground directly and quickly; the flat sheets fall more slowly, perhaps drifting to the ground. Encourage the children to provide explanations relating the force of the air to the shape of the object moving through the air.

Ask the children to make information posters explaining about the force of air. They could include a mixture of annotated drawings, cartoon pictures and precise, scientific statements.

Suggestion(s) for extension
Invite ideas for an investigation to find out what shapes of objects encounter least resistance from the air.

Suggestion(s) for support
Where necessary, help children with their posters by discussing the information they want to include. Help them to compose relevant statements.

Assessment opportunities
Assess the children's awareness and understanding of air resistance as a friction force by discussing their information posters with them. Do they recognize that the air resists the movement of objects? Do they understand that the force of air resistance is greater on an object with a larger surface area? Can they describe examples of objects affected by air resistance?

Display ideas
The children's information posters can be displayed along with relevant pictures, objects and models: umbrellas, kites, sails, flags, parachutes and so on.

Other aspects of the PoS covered
Introduction (Sc0) 1a, b, c; 2a, b; 3b; 4a; 5a, b.

SPRING IS HERE

Because springs exert a force, they can be used in a variety of ways.

†† *Whole-class discussion and exploration, followed by individual recording.*

🕐 *60 minutes.*

⚠ *The children must take care when using and stretching springs.*

Previous skills/knowledge needed
The children should understand that a force is a push or a pull.

Key background information
Springs usually exist in a spiral form, and are made of metal (to particular specifications depending on their intended use). They lose their elasticity if over-stretched, and need careful handling. Plastic springs are sometimes used in children's toys.

Preparation
Collect and check the equipment needed (see below). Make one copy per child of photocopiable page 120.

Resources needed
Springs of various types and sizes, including a large metal spring for demonstration; objects which use springs (such as a stapler, a retractable ballpoint pen, toys, spring balances); photocopiable page 120.

Vocabulary
Spring, spiral, coil, stretch, compress, exert, force.

What to do
Show the children a large metal spring. Ask them to describe what they see and what it is made of. Discuss what the spring does, and demonstrate how it can be stretched and compressed. Talk about the force of the spring; demonstrate how a compressed spring pushes against an object, and how a stretched spring pulls on whatever is stretching it. Provide different springs for the children to handle and compare by pressing and pulling. Emphasize the need for careful handling of springs.

Next, talk about the usefulness of springs. Ask the children for examples of how springs are used to make things 'work'. They might mention toys, retractable pens, spring balances, staplers, sofas, mattresses and cars. Have available as many objects as possible for the children to examine and discuss, looking at the function of the spring(s) in each object.

Give out copies of photocopiable page 120. Ask the children to identify the use of the spring in each picture and explain why it is used. They can add examples of their own, and compile a list of other uses of springs.

Suggestion(s) for extension

Invite the children to suggest ideas and plans for testing how well different springs allow compression, or how well they bounce back.

Suggestion(s) for support

Encourage less confident children to handle the springs and objects, carefully observing the effect of stretching or compressing them. Help the children to write accurate phrases and sentences when they are recording their observations.

Assessment opportunities

Assess the children's understanding of the forces involved during stretching and compression, and their awareness of some uses of springs in everyday life.

Display ideas

Make available a range of different types of springs for the children to handle; include examples of springs within objects. Display pictures of large objects with springs. Write out some questions and statements about the items on display.

Other aspects of the PoS covered

Introduction (Sc0) 1a, b, c; 2a, b; 4a.

Reference to photocopiable sheet

Photocopiable page 120 shows four examples of springs in use. The children can explain how the spring is used in each of the cases illustrated, then provide examples of their own.

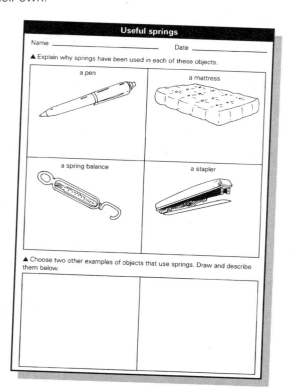

STRETCHING ELASTIC BANDS

We can explore the force acting on an elastic band by measuring how much it stretches.

†† *Whole-class discussion and activity.*

🕐 *20 minutes for introduction; 60 minutes for activity and recording.*

⚠ *The children must take care when stretching elastic bands, and especially guard their eyes.*

Previous skills/knowledge needed

The children should know that a force is a push or a pull, and that an elastic band exerts a force on whatever is stretching it. For the extension activity, they will need to know how to use a force meter.

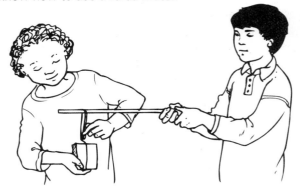

Key background information

Placing a box beneath the suspended elastic band will prevent weights falling on hands and feet. If the measurements are accurate, this activity provides data which can be usefully represented as a line graph.

Preparation

Collect the equipment needed. Find a method of suspending the weights from the elastic band which is safe and allows for accurate measuring. Test various bands so as to provide ones which will safely demonstrate stretching while a number of weights are added (perhaps 100g at a time until 1kg is reached).

Resources needed

Elastic bands of various lengths and thicknesses; an S-shaped hook; a firm rod; weights which can be suspended from a hook (or in a net bag); a large box or bin; a ruler or tape measure; squared paper; force meters (see extension activity).

Vocabulary

Force, elastic band, exert, stretch, suspend, weights.

What to do

Talk about the properties of elastic bands: they are made of a material which can be stretched, but will return to its original shape and size. Discuss how they are used to hold things together: pencils, banknotes and so on. Tell the children that you want them to explore the force acting on an elastic band by measuring the lengths to which it will stretch when different weights are added.

Remind the children about safety precautions: elastic bands can be overstretched and break, or can flick back painfully; feet and hands must be kept away from suspended weights, which might fall at any time. Decide how to organize the test – for example, looping an elastic band over a rod and attaching weights by means of a hook. The children need to try out the method of suspension, so that they can decide how to make their measurements. Encourage them to plan a systematic method of working. Depending on the elastic band they are using, advise them on which weights to use; they might start with 100g and add further 100g weights until 1kg is reached, so that a pattern emerges from the data. Children can test similar bands so that the measurements can be checked, or different bands so that their stretchiness can be compared. Prepare a chart for recording the measurements. Make sure the children understand exactly how the length of the band will be measured, and that accuracy is very important.

The children can use their data to draw line graphs. Talk about what these show, and discuss the pattern which emerges. *Did the length of the elastic band increase by the same amount each time a weight was added? Do you think it would continue to stretch in the same way if more and more weights were added?* Ask the children to use the graph to predict the length of the elastic band for in-between weights, and for further weights. Test these predictions if possible. Ask the children what this particular band might be useful for. *How big a roll of paper would it hold?*

Ask the children to record this activity by making a set of instructions (as annotated diagrams) for others to use.

Suggestion(s) for extension

Instead of using weights, some children could use a force meter to measure the force required to stretch different elastic bands. They could measure the lengths to which each band will stretch when a force of 1, 2, 3 or more

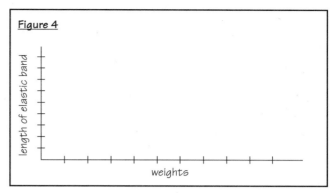

Figure 4

length of elastic band / *weights*

newtons is applied. Ask them whether a thicker band always stretches more than a thinner one.

Suggestion(s) for support

For children who have difficulty in drawing a line graph, provide partly labelled axes (see Figure 4). Give further help with plotting the points if necessary.

Assessment opportunities

During the activity, talk to the children to assess their understanding of the force exerted by the stretched elastic band. Do they understand that the greater the length to which the band stretches, the greater is the force opposing the pull of the weights? Assess their understanding of line graphs. Can they interpret a graph and identify patterns in the data shown?

Opportunities for IT

The children can use data handling software to store their data and present the results as a line graph.

Display ideas

Display various types and sizes of elastic bands, and start a class list of their uses. Display the children's instructions and graphs, and draw a large line graph with clear labels (which can be used when discussing patterns in the results).

Other aspects of the PoS covered

Introduction (Sc0) 1a, b, c, d; 2a; 4a, b, c; 5a, b. Experimental and investigative science (Sc1) 2a, b; 3a, b, c.

BALANCED FORCES

When an object is at rest, the forces acting on it are balanced.

†† *Whole-class discussion, followed by individual recording.*

🕐 *30 minutes for discussion; 30 minutes for recording.*

Previous skills/knowledge needed

The children should be aware of a range of forces: magnetism; friction, including air and water resistance; stretching and compression of springs; the stretching of elastic bands; and gravity.

Key background information

The force of gravity pulls everything downwards. When an object is at rest on the ground, the upward force of the ground pushing back is equal and opposite to the force of gravity. On a diagram, a force can be represented by an arrow. Where opposing forces are balanced, the arrows should be the same size.

Preparation

Make one copy per child of photocopiable page 121.

Vocabulary

Forces, balanced, stationary, still, at rest, suspended, movement, magnetic, magnetism, attract, friction, air resistance, water resistance, upthrust, gravity, weight, stretching, compressing.

Resources needed

Photocopiable page 121, pencils.

What to do

Remind the children of the range of forces they have experienced in previous work. Talk about magnetic forces, gravity, friction (including air and water resistance), the

compression and stretching of springs and the stretching of elastic bands. Then ask one child to lie down, very still, on the floor. Ask the class what forces are acting on this child. Explain that there are two forces acting on the child; discuss the relationship between the force of gravity pushing the body downwards and the force of the floor reacting against gravity and pushing upwards. Ask the children what would happen if there were no upward force from the floor.

Ask two children to push gently against each other by pressing the palms of their right hands together. Encourage them to reach a state where they are both quite still, and therefore the two pushing forces are equal. Explain that because the forces are balanced, the hands remain still.

Ask the children to point out other objects in the classroom which have balanced forces acting upon them – which could be any stationary thing. Use a drawing of an object on a table to show the children how to draw force diagrams using arrows; since the object is still, the forces are balanced and so the arrows are the same size. (See Figure 5.) Discuss balanced forces involving magnetism (a paper clip at rest between two magnets), the upthrust of water (a plastic duck floating), air resistance (a piece of paper hovering for a moment in the air) and stretch (a weight suspended from an elastic band).

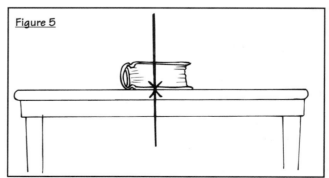

Figure 5

Give out copies of photocopiable page 121; discuss the situations with the children if necessary. Ask the children to draw a pair of equal-sized arrows in each picture to represent the equal forces, and to write a short description of those forces.

Suggestion(s) for extension
Children could go on to consider a tug of war in which the two teams are balanced, and draw a force diagram (showing the horizontal forces only).

Suggestion(s) for support
If necessary, discuss each picture on photocopiable page 121 with the children. Help them to write a concise description of each pair of forces.

Assessment opportunities
Assess the children's overall grasp of the idea of balanced forces in relation to a variety of situations. Do they understand that two equal and opposed forces acting on any stationary object will cause it to remain stationary?

Display ideas
The children can turn their own drawings and paintings into diagrams of balanced forces, labelling them with the names of the different forces and attaching cut-out arrows.

Other aspects of the PoS covered
Introduction (Sc0) 1a; 2a, b; 4a.

Reference to photocopiable sheet
Photocopiable page 121 shows some examples of situations involving balanced forces. The children can add arrows to represent the forces, and write a description of the forces involved.

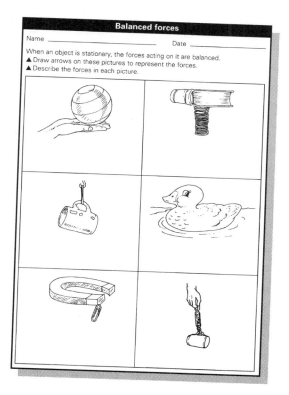

WEIGHT IN AIR AND WATER

Objects weigh less in water than in air, because of the upward force of the water. We can use a force meter to demonstrate this.

†† *Whole-class introduction, followed by work in groups of three or four.*

🕐 *60 minutes.*

Previous skills/knowledge needed
The children need to know that a force is a push or a pull. They should understand that objects have weight because of the pull of gravity. They need to have handled a force meter, understand that it is used to measure forces, know how it works and have practised reading the scale.

Key background information
The upward force of water on an object is called the **upthrust**. An object suspended in water is subjected to this force, which opposes gravity. The upthrust of water is greater than the upthrust of air, so objects appear to weigh less when submerged in water than when in air. (Note that upthrust and resistance to movement are not the same, since upthrust affects objects that are not moving.)

Preparation
Check the force meters to be used. Fill some large containers with water. Make one copy per child of photocopiable page 122.

Resources needed
Force meters; large, deep containers (such as plastic bowls); a ball or empty plastic bottle; objects (suitable for weighing) which will sink in water; objects which will float in water (see extension activity); photocopiable page 122.

Vocabulary

Force, weight, force meter, newtons, gravity, upthrust, suspended.

What to do

Ask the children what they know about the force of water; they may remember that water resists movement. Tell them that water also has an upward force or **upthrust** which supports floating objects. This can be demonstrated by letting a child push a ball or an empty plastic bottle into water. Say that the upward force of water on a submerged object can be measured using a force meter; and that the upthrust of air can be compared with that of water by weighing something in air and then in water. Remind the children how to use a force meter, and that the unit of force is the newton.

Working in groups of three or four, the children can choose several objects to weigh in air using a force meter. They should avoid using objects which would float in water. They can use photocopiable page 122 to record their measurements. Encourage them to work in an organized manner, taking turns to hold the force meter and read the scale. Point out that at least two children should make each reading in order to ensure accuracy. Next, the same objects can be weighed in water. Demonstrate how this should be done, with the object completely submerged but not resting on the bottom of the container. Again, measurements can be recorded on the chart.

Discuss the results, looking for patterns. The children will find that each object weighs less when submerged in water. Point out that gravity gives objects their weight. Encourage explanations which refer to the downward force of gravity against the upthrust of air or water: the water pushes upwards and opposes gravity with more force than the air. Because of the relatively strong opposing force of water, the objects weigh less.

Ask the children to draw diagrams of the same object suspended in air and in water, using arrows to represent the forces acting on the object. They should draw the same size of arrow to represent gravity in both cases, but draw a bigger arrow to represent the upthrust of water than that used to represent the upthrust of air.

Suggestion(s) for extension

Introduce some objects which float in water, and ask a group of children to weigh them as they float. They will discover that the reading on the force meter is zero. Encourage them to explain this in terms of balanced forces.

Suggestion(s) for support

If children find taking force meter readings difficult, ask them to check the readings with you. Help with interpreting the scale if necessary.

Assessment opportunities

Use the children's force diagrams to assess how well they understand the idea that water exerts a greater upward force against gravity than air, causing an object to weigh less in water than in air. Assess their skills in using a force meter and recording results accurately.

Opportunities for IT

The children can use data handling software to store and retrieve results and to present them as a table.

Display ideas

Produce a large table chart which collects together measurements from all the groups. Use labels and statements to convey the children's explanations.

Other aspects of the PoS covered

Introduction (Sc0) 1a, b, c, d; 2a; 4a, b, c. Experimental and investigative science (Sc1) 2a, b.

Reference to photocopiable sheet

The children can use photocopiable page 122 to record their measurements, comments and explanations during and after the activity.

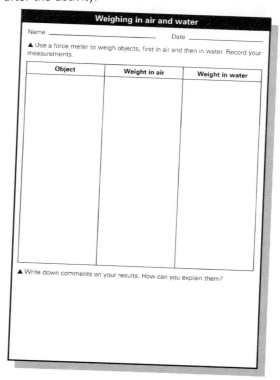

TRANSPARENT AND OPAQUE

Transparent materials and objects allow a lot of light to pass through them; opaque materials and objects do not let any light pass through them.

†† *Whole-class introduction; small groups for planning and testing; whole-class discussion.*

⊕ *20 minutes introduction; 60 minutes planning, testing and recording; 30–40 minutes discussion and final recording.*

Previous skills/knowledge needed

The children should understand that light travels in straight lines from a source, and that a shadow is formed when light is blocked and cannot pass through an object. They should be aware that some materials (known as **transparent** materials) allow light to pass through.

Key background information

We know that light travels in straight lines because it creates an area of darkness, a **shadow**, when it is blocked by an object. **Opaque** materials block all light. **Transparent** materials block only a small amount of light, casting a faint shadow. **Translucent** materials allow light to pass through, but the light is blurred (**diffused**) and makes a pattern of faint shadows.

Preparation

Collect a range of materials and objects for testing (see below). Check the torches. Make one copy per child of photocopiable page 123.

Resources needed

A piece of opaque flexible tubing (like the kind used to connect washing machines and dishwashers to drains); photocopiable page 123. For each group, a collection of materials and objects: some opaque (corrugated card, thick paper, a wooden ruler), some transparent (a plastic bottle, clear and coloured cellophane, a glass jar) and some translucent (greaseproof paper, thin 'see-through' fabric, bubble wrap); also materials with holes (such as a piece of mesh), a powerful torch, a piece of white card.

Vocabulary

Light, light source, shadow, opaque, transparent, translucent.

What to do

Ask the children to explain how they know that light travels in a straight line. If necessary, refer to the shadow made when light from a source is blocked. Use a torch and a piece of opaque flexible tubing to demonstrate that light does not bend (see Figure 6). Show the children the collection of items. Ask: *Which items do you think will not let any light through? Do you remember the word*

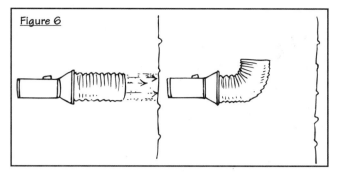

Figure 6

opaque? Which items will let the most light through? Do you think the bubble wrap will let as much light pass through as the clear polythene does? Can light pass through greaseproof paper? What about a piece of netting?

Ask the children how they could find out how much light passes through each material and how much is blocked. Remind them that a shadow is formed when light is blocked. Say that you want them to investigate to find out which of the items form shadows. They can use a torch and a piece of white card as a screen.

Planning

Encourage the children to use their knowledge of light and shadows to predict, for each item, whether or not a shadow will be formed when a light is shone on it. Then they should organize a method of working. They could make a list of instructions for themselves, such as:

1. We will shine the torch on each item in turn, holding it in front of the screen.
2. We will look carefully to see whether there is a shadow.
3. We will write down our observations, describing the shadow in detail.

Photocopiable page 123 can be used for recording predictions and observations.

Obtaining evidence

Insist on careful observations and detailed recording. Ask questions such as: *What is the shape of the shadow? Is it the same shape as the object? Is the shadow easy to see? Can you describe the pattern of light and shadow? Which parts of the* [transparent] *object produced a faint shadow?*

Considering evidence

Discuss the results as a class. *Which items can be truly described as opaque? Which items can be truly described as transparent? Does everyone agree? Were you surprised that some 'transparent' objects made a shadow? Was there any difference between the shadow made by the card and the one made by the greaseproof paper? Was the pattern of the netting like the pattern of light and shadow it made?* Compare the observations made by the groups; sort out any differences, and encourage the children to accept generalizations.

Help the children to conclude that some materials and objects do not let any light through and form dark shadows.

Others let most of the light through, but still make a faint shadow. Encourage the children to decide whether their observations support their predictions, and to explain any unexpected results. Ask them to write a paragraph about what they have discovered.

Suggestion(s) for extension
Introduce the term **translucent**. Ask a group of children to write lists of opaque, transparent and translucent materials and objects, starting with those in the classroom.

Suggestion(s) for support
Where necessary, assist with writing to make sure that all the children have a detailed record of their observations.

Assessment opportunities
Assess the children's scientific attitude. Do they write down exactly what they see? Are they willing to revise their ideas in the light of evidence?

Display ideas
The sorted collection of materials can be displayed, along with the children's observations and conclusions.

Other aspects of the PoS covered
Introduction (Sc0) 1a, b, c; 2a, b; 4a. Experimental and investigative science 1a, b; 2a, b; 3b, c, d, e. Materials and their properties 1a.

Reference to photocopiable sheet
The children can use the framework on page 123 to record their predictions when planning the test and their observations when carrying out the test.

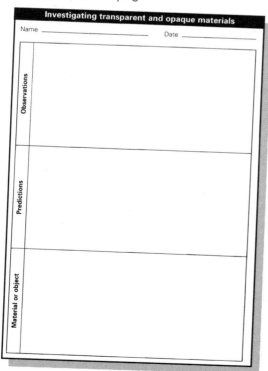

LIGHT GETS IN YOUR EYES

We see objects when light reflected from them enters our eyes.

†† *Whole class discussion and demonstration; individual recording.*

🕐 *60 minutes.*

⚠ *Warn the children of the dangers of looking directly at the Sun, or any other bright light source.*

Previous skills/knowledge needed
The children need to know that light travels in straight lines from a source, and that it can be reflected by objects.

Key background information
During this activity, be aware of any children with impaired vision; discuss any problems sensitively, and make sure that all the children take as great a part in the session as possible.

On reaching a transparent object, most of the light from a source will pass through the object. On reaching an opaque object, most of the light will be blocked; some will be absorbed, some reflected. Any of the reflected light reaching our eyes will enable us to see the object.

Preparation
Arrange a darkened area. Make one copy per child of photocopiable page 124.

Resources needed
Several torches providing different intensities of light; photocopiable page 124; pictures, books and other reference sources about how we see.

Vocabulary
Light, source, beam, travelling, enter, direction.

What to do
Talk about light sources: the Sun, a torch, a flame, a light bulb, fireflies and so on. Ask the children to explain how we are able to see these things. Elicit the reply that light from these sources enters our eyes, enabling us to see them. Warn the children not to look directly at the Sun.

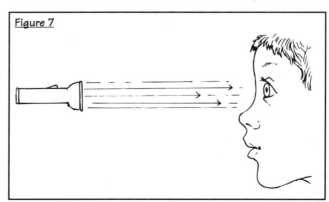

Figure 7

Use a small, not too bright torch in a darkened area to demonstrate how the light can enter our eyes directly when the torch is shone in our faces. Help the children to draw a diagram showing this (as in Figure 7).

Discuss how our eyes see other objects because light from a source is reflected from them. Explain that when light shines on an object, it is reflected in all directions; some of it reaches our eyes when we look towards the object, enabling us to see it. If we close our eyes, the light is prevented from reaching them and we do not see. The more light is reflected from an object, the brighter it will appear. Shine some light sources of different intensities on an object to show this.

Encourage the children to draw diagrams to represent any of the situations demonstrated, and to use reference sources to find out more about how light enables us to see. Give out copies of photocopiable page 124; ask the children to draw arrows showing how the people in the drawings see the objects, and then to draw a diagram showing how they see the page (see Figure 8).

Figure 8

Suggestion(s) for extension
A group of children could use a torch and a piece of white paper to explore what happens to a beam of light when it reaches a mirror, and draw diagrams to show how the direction of the light changes (see Figure 9).

Suggestion(s) for support
Where necessary, help by emphasizing the direction that light will take from source to object, and from object to eye. Show how arrows can represent this sequence in a diagram.

Assessment opportunities
Use the children's recording on the photocopiable sheet to assess their understanding of how we see. Have they drawn arrows to indicate the path of the light correctly? Do their diagrams show that light is reflected from an object they see into their eyes?

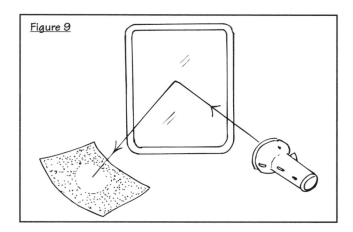

Figure 9

Opportunities for IT
The children could produce diagrams using graphics software, with red or yellow lines to represent rays of light.

Display ideas
Create a large, cartoon-like picture of people, objects and light sources. Provide cut-out arrows which children can attach to the picture to show how we see things. The children's diagrams can be displayed alongside.

Other aspects of the PoS covered
Introduction (Sc0) 1a, b, c; 2a; 4a, c; 5a, b.

Reference to photocopiable sheet
Photocopiable page 124 provides four pictures on which the children can draw arrows to represent the path of light to human eyes. They can also draw a diagram to show how they see the page.

CHANGING SHADOWS

We can find out more about how the size and position of a shadow changes by carrying out an investigation.

†† *Whole-class introduction, then whole-class or small-group investigation.*

🕐 *60 minutes discussion and planning; 60 minutes testing and recording.*

Previous skills/knowledge needed

The children need to understand that shadows are formed when light from a source is blocked, and that shadows can change. They should be aware that changing one factor and keeping all other factors the same is important when investigating. They should be able to present data as a line graph.

Key background information

The nearer an opaque object is to a light source, the larger the shadow is, since more light is blocked. The children can measure how far an object is from a screen or a light source, and plot either distance on a line graph against the size of the shadow cast.

Preparation

Check the light sources to be used. Arrange a darkened area with a flat surface between a light source and a wall; attach a large sheet of paper or card to the wall as a screen. Make one copy per child of photocopiable page 125.

Resources needed

One or more sources of light (such as powerful torches); a suitable wall; a large sheet of paper or card; rulers or tape meaures; squared paper; pens and pencils; photocopiable page 125.

Vocabulary

Light source, screen, distance, opaque.

What to do

In a darkened area, switch on a bright light source such as a powerful torch or an overhead projector beam. Ask a child to make a shadow on a screen, using an object such as a pencil, and then to change the shadow by moving the object. *What happens to the shadow?* Encourage the children to comment on any changes they notice. Tell the children that you want them to find out the relationship between the size of the shadow and the distance the object is from **either** the light source **or** the screen. To do this, they will need to carry out an investigation.

Planning

One investigation can be carried out by the whole class, or small groups of children can organize their own tests.

Decide on a question to investigate, such as: *What happens to the shadow as the object is moved nearer to the source of light?* Discuss how the test will be organized so that measurements can be taken efficiently. *What units will we use? Will a tape measure or a ruler be best? How can we arrange the light source and screen so that measuring will be accurate? Is it a good idea to move the object by regular rather than random distances?*

Consider the factors which will need to be kept the same: the position of the screen, the position of the light source and the method of taking measurements. The variable will be the distance of the object from the screen or light source; this should be measured whenever it is changed. The height of the shadow can be measured by marking the screen. Photocopiable page 125 can be used as a planning aid; the children will also need to draw a chart for the measurements.

Obtaining evidence

Point out the importance of accurate measuring, both of the variable being changed and of the height of the shadow. Ask the children to remind you which factors they are keeping the same, and how they are changing the variable.

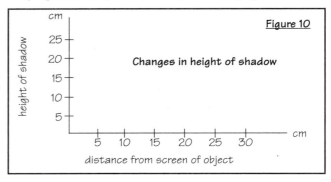

Considering evidence

Help the children to draw a line graph (see Figure 10), and encourage them to identify a pattern in their results. Look for any measurements which might need checking because they do not fit the pattern. Ask the children to 'read off' a result from their graph for an intermediate distance that they did not actually use. Encourage them to reach the conclusion that the nearer the object was to the light source (**or** the further it was from the screen), the bigger the shadow was.

Ask the children to write a scientific account of how the test was carried out and what the results show. Prompt with questions or sentence openers if necessary: *What have you found out from this investigation? The shadow gets bigger when... How do you know that your results are reliable? Because the test was... and the measuring was...*

Suggestion(s) for extension

A group of children could devise a shadow puppet play with figures whose shadows change in size during the performance. They could use measurements to plot the positions that the puppets will need to take.

Suggestion(s) for support

Where necessary, provide the framework for the line graph and guide the chidren towards labelling the axes and plotting the measurements.

Assessment opportunities

Use discussion and the children's scientific accounts to assess their understanding of the investigation. Do they recognize that the test has demonstrated a consistent relationship between the light source, the object and the shadow? Do they understand that a line graph is useful because it shows the results as a pattern?

Opportunities for IT

The children can use data handling software to store and retrieve results, and to present them as a graph.

Display ideas

Create a large picture of a light source and two different-sized shadows as a focal point for a display of the children's planning notes and line graphs, including a boldly written or printed statement of the overall conclusion reached.

Other aspects of the PoS covered

Introduction (Sc0) 1a, b, c, d; 2a, b; 4a, b, c. Experimental and investigative science (Sc1) 1a, c, d; 2a, b, c; 3a, b, c.

Reference to photocopiable sheet

The children can use photocopiable page 125 to plan their investigation.

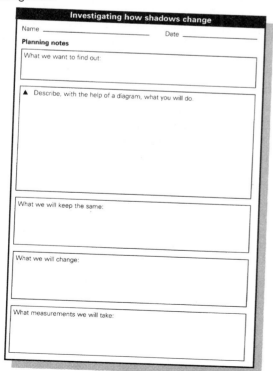

SHADOWS AND REFLECTIONS

The differences between shadows and reflections tell us a lot about the behaviour of light.

✝✝ *Whole-class discussion, followed by individual recording.*

🕐 *45 minutes.*

Previous skills/knowledge needed

The children should have explored shadows and reflections in previous work. They should know how shadows are formed, and that an image is produced when most of the light is reflected from an object.

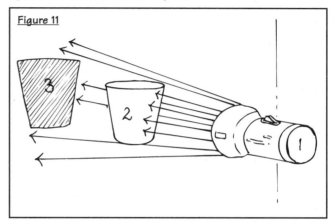

Key background information

When light reaches an opaque object, it is prevented from travelling further; a dark unlit area is formed behind the object. This is a **shadow**. (See Figure 11.) Some of the light reaching the object is absorbed and some is reflected. Most of the light that hits a **mirror** type of surface is reflected. When this light is reflected back into our eyes, we see an image of the object it has come from. This is a **reflection**. (See Figure 12.)

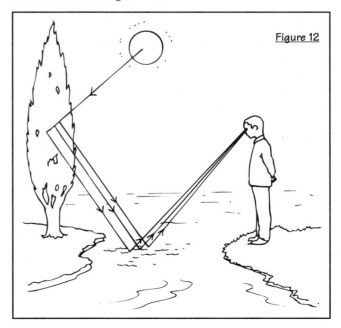

Preparation

Collect a range of reflective materials: unbreakable or safety mirrors, metal objects, shiny paper and shiny fabrics.

Resources needed

Torches; a collection of reflective materials (see above); a small opaque object such as a pencil; a sheet of white paper.

Vocabulary

Light, shadow, opaque, reflection, reflect, direction, shiny, mirror.

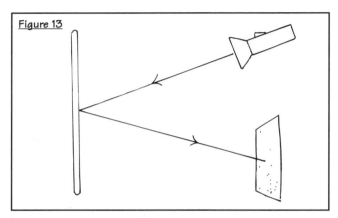

Figure 13

What to do

Review the children's experience of shadows and how they are formed; encourage the use of terms such as *light, travels, opaque, blocked.* Explain that when the light reaches an object, it may be **absorbed** by the object: it may disappear into the object and travel no further. Shine the beam from a torch onto a small opaque object, and ask a child to use a piece of string to represent the path of the light from the torch to the object. Use a longer piece of string to demonstrate how light will continue to travel where there is nothing to stop it.

Now explain that although some of the light is absorbed, some will bounce back from the object into our eyes, enabling us to see the object. Use a torch beam to show how the light is reflected by a mirror. Ask a child to shine the torch onto the mirror at an angle; another child can position a sheet of white paper to 'catch' the beam as it is reflected (see Figure 13). Ask the children to predict where they will need to hold the paper if you change the angle of the beam of light.

Tell the children that smooth, flat, shiny surfaces reflect the most light. *When you look at a mirror, most of the light from your face is reflected back to your eyes. You see an image of yourself which is called a* **reflection.** Ask the children what other things produce a reflection. They may suggest shiny paper, metal objects and water. Explain that a shiny surface is shiny because most of the light that hits it bounces back.

Ask the children to tell you what the differences are between shadows and reflections. For example: a shadow

is dark, a reflection is usually bright; a shadow is only a shape, a reflection shows details; a shadow is made when light is blocked by an opaque material, a reflection is made when light changes direction as it hits a shiny surface. Provide pairs of children with a torch and some reflective materials; ask them to explore the differences between shadows and reflections, recording what they find in words, drawings and diagrams. *How did you make a shadow? How do you make a reflection? Describe and draw what you did. What differences do you see between a shadow and a reflection?*

Suggestion(s) for extension

Some children could go on to sort reflective surfaces according to the type of reflected image they produce: accurate, distorted or shadowy.

Suggestion(s) for support

If some children are confused, show them a shadow and a reflection side by side so that they can observe the differences more easily.

Assessment opportunities

The children's diagrams will help to indicate their understanding of how shadows and reflections are formed and the differences between them.

Opportunities for IT

The children could use graphics software to produce diagrams of shadows and reflections, showing filled and reversed-out areas, coloured light rays and reversed images.

Display ideas

Use matt black paper and aluminium foil as contrasting backing for work on shadows and work on reflections, with samples of appropriate materials.

Other aspects of the PoS covered

(Sc0) 1a; 2a; 4a, b.

TRAVELLING SOUNDS

Sound vibrations can travel through various materials before they reach our ears.

✝✝ *Whole-class discussion; paired exploration; individual recording.*

🕐 *45 minutes discussion and exploration; 40 minutes recording.*

⚠ *Remind the children that very loud sounds can damage the ears.*

Previous skills/knowledge needed

The children should know that there are many sources of sounds, and that sounds are made when objects vibrate.

Key background information

During this activity, be aware of any children with impaired hearing; discuss any problems sensitively, and make sure that all the children take as great a part in the session as possible.

Sounds travel through solids, liquids and gases by causing the molecules of the material to vibrate. Sounds cannot travel through a vacuum, as there is nothing there to vibrate.

Preparation

Find some objects around the school which will carry a sound – for example, a water pipe or a set of railings. Collect various materials which will carry a sound (see 'What to do'). Attach a plastic cup to each end of a long piece of string. Wrap a loudly ticking clock inside some waterproof material.

Resources needed

A torch; sound-carrying materials (see below); a plastic tank or bucket; plastic cups; string; a clock with a loud tick; waterproof material; paper, writing materials; plastic string and fishing line (see extension activity).

Vocabulary

Sound, vibrate, travel, solid, liquid, gas, air.

What to do

Arrange for two children with a torch to stand outside the classroom. Close the door. At an agreed moment, the pair should switch on the torch and announce in loud voices what they are doing. Ask the children in the classroom: *Could you see the light from the torch? Could you hear the voices?* Point out that the beam of light was prevented from reaching their eyes, since it was blocked by the walls and door. However, the sound waves of the voices were able to travel through the materials of the classroom wall and door to reach the children's ears.

Ask the children to suggest other things through which sound can travel. They may have heard recordings of the sounds that whales or dolphins make when communicating with each other over long distances underwater; they may mention the sound of a heartbeat travelling through the body and being heard by a doctor with a stethoscope; they may have heard sounds transmitted by water pipes at home. Tell them how the native Americans listened with an ear to the ground, to pick up any sounds of approaching animals or enemies.

Give the children opportunities to experience sounds travelling through a range of materials by suggesting that they try passing sounds through and along various objects: wooden (a table top, a bookshelf, a window sill, a broom handle, a fence); metal (a pipe, railings); plastic (a piece of pipe, a table top) and brick (a wall). They could also experiment with a string telephone: a length of string with a plastic cup on each end. One child can tap or speak into one cup, while a partner puts an ear to the other cup. *Which sounds travel best along the string?*

Demonstrate how sound travels through water by wrapping a loudly ticking clock in waterproof material and submerging it in a bucket of water. *Can you still hear the sound when the clock is in the water? Does it sound the same? How can it be heard best – by listening from above; by putting your ear to the container? What is the sound travelling through to get to our ears?* (The waterproof wrapping, the water, the container and the air.)

Focus on sounds travelling through the air by asking the children to listen and record all the sounds they can hear when in the playground. *What is the most distant sound you can hear? Are sounds coming from every direction? Is there anything which could be blocking the sounds?*

Finally, ask the children to draw and annotate simple diagrams to show an example each of a sound travelling through a solid, a liquid and a gas. They should use a different colour to represent the sound waves in each diagram.

Suggestion(s) for extension

A group of children could compare how sound travels through ordinary string, plastic string and plastic fishing line by attaching identical lengths to plastic cups and transmitting sounds (taps) across a fixed distance.

Suggestion(s) for support

Where necessary, help children to identify examples of sound travelling through a solid, a liquid and a gas, and to record these as diagrams.

Assessment opportunities

Use the children's diagrams to assess their understanding of how sounds travel through different materials.

Display ideas

Create a display in three areas of the classroom to show examples of sounds travelling through solids, liquids and gases. Use pictures, diagrams and sentences. Where possible, provide actual examples for the children to explore.

Other aspects of the PoS covered

Introduction (Sc0) 1a, b, c; 2a; 4a, c.

KEEPING IT QUIET

Some materials are useful in preventing sound from reaching our ears. To make reliable comparisons, we must plan an investigation.

†† *Whole-class discussion; whole-class or group investigation.*

🕐 *20 minutes introduction; 60 minutes planning; 60 minutes testing and recording.*

⚠ *Remind the children that very loud sounds can damage the ears.*

Previous skills/knowledge needed

The children need to know that sounds are made when objects vibrate, and that sounds can travel through a range of materials.

Key background information

As hearing ability varies between individuals, it can be difficult to agree about what is a loud noise and when there is no sound at all. Loud and continuous sounds can cause permanent damage to hearing. Be sensitive to children with any degree of hearing impairment, and provide appropriate support.

Sound travels more easily through some materials than others. Some materials absorb sound waves, preventing them from travelling further. These materials include foam rubber, polystyrene, cardboard and some fabrics. They are useful as a means of reducing sound levels. Lining walls, padding noisy machinery parts and planting trees next to motorways are all ways of limiting sound.

Preparation

Collect the materials needed. Check the suitability of the sound source to be used in the investigation.

Resources needed

An independent sound source such as a loudly ticking clock or noisy toy; a range of materials for soundproofing such as various fabrics, bubble wrap, foam rubber, newspaper; pictures representing noisy situations; reference sources relating to soundproofing methods.

Vocabulary

Sound, vibration, travel, protect, muffle, soundproof.

What to do

Discuss the variety of sounds which reach our ears during the course of a day: soft sounds, sounds we consider normal, and unpleasantly loud noises. Point out that loud sounds are disruptive and can be annoying; if continuous, they can damage our ears. Talk about ways of minimizing sound: closing doors, drawing curtains, installing carpets and so on. Tell the children that trees are planted alongside motorways and other busy roads to reduce the traffic noise reaching nearby homes. With the children's help, list people who experience loud sounds in their work; discuss how they protect their hearing.

Tell the children that you want them to find out which materials are useful for preventing sound from travelling. Suggest that they think of ways to muffle the sound of a ticking clock. Show them a range of materials they could test, and ask them to consider how they can make comparisons. *How can we find out which of these materials is best at preventing sound from travelling? How could we use the materials to prevent us from hearing the clock?*

Planning

Consider all of the children's ideas before choosing one. They might suggest wrapping the clock in the material and measuring how far away they need to be so as not to hear any sound; or staying in the same place and counting how many layers of the material are required before the sound is completely muffled. Encourage the children to predict which material will be the most effective, and to record and justify their predictions. Ask them to describe how the test will be made fair, and what evidence they will collect. Use questions to help the children record their planning: *What do we want to find out? What equipment and materials will we use? Which material do you think will be the best at preventing sound from travelling? How will we organize our test? What will we keep the same? What will be changed? What evidence will we need to collect? What problems might we have when deciding whether the sound can be heard?* Help the children to draw a suitable chart on which to record their observations.

Obtaining evidence

The children can carry out the investigation as a class or in groups. Help them to carry out a fair test carefully, following their plans and recording the evidence they collect. Ask: *What are we doing to make sure our test is fair? Does everyone agree about how much sound is reaching our ears? Are we wrapping the clock in the same way for each type of material?*

Considering evidence

Discuss any problems encountered in keeping the test fair, and in making comparisons between the different materials. *Was it easy to decide when the sound had faded out? Did everyone agree about when they could not hear the sound? How reliable is this evidence? Would a different group of people obtain the same results?* Talk about the predictions made and whether they match the results.

Ask the children to write an account of the test, describing any problems and trying to explain what they have found out. Ask: *Why are some materials better than others for sound-proofing?* (They absorb sound more easily and prevent it from passing through.) *Is there anything*

special/similar about materials which are good at preventing sound from travelling? (They feel thick or bulky and contain lots of air spaces.)

Suggestion(s) for extension

A group of children could plan and carry out another test independently. They could investigate which material is best for making ear defenders, or use boxes as models to find out which material is best for soundproofing a room.

Suggestion(s) for support

Where necessary, provide guidance with planning and carrying out a fair test. If there is disagreement about levels of sound, talk to individual children about what they can hear.

Assessment opportunities

Note whether the children understand that some materials prevent sound from travelling more effectively than others. Assess their scientific approach to the investigation: do they carry out a fair test and collect reliable evidence?

Opportunities for IT

The children can write and present their accounts of the investigation using a word processor, including labelled diagrams drawn using graphics software.

Display ideas

Arrange different materials which could be used for muffling sound. Write out all the children's suggestions for the investigation, and display these to emphasize the importance of every contribution. Display the children's planning and final accounts where they can be read by a wider audience.

Other aspects of the PoS covered

Introduction (Sc0) 1a, b, c, d; 2a, b; 4a, c; Experimental and investigative science (Sc1) 1a, b, c, d, e; 2a, b; 3b, c, d, e.

TRACKING THE SUN'S PATH

The Sun's apparent movement across the sky each day can be followed by observing the changes in light and shadows.

✝✝ *Whole-class activity.*

🕐 *45 minutes introduction and planning; 5–10 minutes daily for observation in classroom; 40 minutes for outdoor observation and recording.*

⚠ *Remind the children that looking directly at the Sun will damage their eyes.*

Previous skills/knowledge needed

The children should understand that shadows are formed when the light from the Sun is blocked by opaque objects, and that shadows formed by the Sun change their positions during the day. They should be aware of the four compass points.

Key background information

The position of the Sun appears to change throughout the day, because the Earth turns on its **axis** in an anti-clockwise direction. Because the Earth's axis is tilted relative to the plane of its orbit around the Sun, more of the Sun's light and heat reaches the **northern hemisphere** for half of its orbit, resulting in summer. Meanwhile, the **southern hemisphere** is in winter. For the second half of the orbit, the situations are reversed.

Preparation

Find a suitable area for observing the Sun's light and shadows, if the classroom is inappropriate. Make a large circular direction indicator (see Figure 14) suitable for outdoor use, or ask the children to make their own smaller versions. Use a compass to determine and mark the direction north.

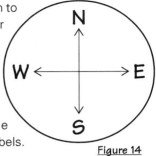

Figure 14

Resources needed

A directional indicator (see above); a compass; adhesive labels.

Vocabulary

Sun, shadow, light, travel, pattern, highest, shortest, direction.

What to do

Choose a day when it is bright and shadows are evident; find another location if the classroom is not suitable. Warning the children never to look directly at the Sun, ask them to decide where the Sun is in the sky. Ask: *How can you tell where the Sun is without looking at it?* Perhaps they looked carefully at shadows, or felt warmth in a particular direction.

Ask the children whether they know where the Sun is at other times during the day, and in which direction it appears to be moving. *What clues are there? Does anyone notice the Sun shining into their bedroom when they wake up? Who sits in the Sun in the classroom during the morning, but not in the afternoon? At what time of day does the classroom become hottest in the summer? What do you remember about going home after school in the winter? At what time of day do we turn on the lights in winter?* Compare this with summer evenings, and talk about the children's winter and summer evening activities.

Suggest devising a more methodical approach to observing the position of the Sun each day. Find three positions within the classroom, or elsewhere in the building, where the Sun shines: (1) during the morning, between 9 and 10 am; (2) at midday; (3) late in the afternoon. In each place, put an object in the sunlight or an adhesive label on the window to indicate where the Sun's rays reach. As a class, make observations over several bright days and discuss the regular pattern of change. Make sure the children understand that the direction in which the Sun appears to move is the same every day. Encourage them to observe the Sun's position in relation to their own homes – perhaps checking it each day when they leave for school and when they return home.

Go on to talk about the four compass points. With the help of a correctly aligned directional indicator, the children can discover that the Sun appears to rise in the east and set in the west; it is highest in the sky at midday. In summer, the Sun is overhead at midday and its path is longer; in winter, its path is shorter. If possible, discuss the Sun's daily path as it can be observed both inside and outside the building.

Discuss how we can take advantage of the position of the Sun at different times of the day. *How could you design a house to have the Sun shining in your bedroom in the morning? On which side of the house is it best to have a patio? Why do so many churches have a stained-glass window in their east-facing wall?* Ask the children to draw diagrams to show the Sun's path in relation to a familiar building, including the compass points.

Suggestion(s) for extension
Some children could compare the paths of the Sun in winter and summer in more detail, drawing annotated diagrams to show the differences.

Suggestion(s) for support
Where necessary, assist with drawing diagrams by suggesting appropriate labels and giving clues about compass points.

Assessment opportunities
Use the children's diagrams to assess their understanding of the path taken by the Sun each day, including the relevant compass points.

Display ideas
Cut out shapes to represent the Sun, the school and appropriate landmarks; with the children's help, arrange these to show the Sun's path. Indicate directions, and add statements relating to winter and summer.

Other aspects of the PoS covered
Introduction (Sc0) 1a, b, c; 2a; 3b; 4a, c ; 5a, b.

SUNRISE AND SUNSET

The Sun rises in the east and sets in the west at predictable times. Graphs are useful for interpreting information.

†† *Whole-class discussion and observation; individual recording.*

⊕ *60 minutes for discussion and recording; 10 minutes each morning and afternoon for observations.*

⚠ *Remind the children never to look directly at the Sun.*

Previous skills/knowledge needed
The children should be aware that the Earth spins on its axis, and that the Sun appears to trace a path across the sky each day.

Key background information
The times of sunrise and sunset throughout the year can be found in newspapers and diaries. They have been calculated precisely by scientists (physicists and astronomers). The times vary for places at different longitudes, as the sunrise reaches eastern points earlier. The times also vary for different latitudes, due to the tilt of the Earth: the more northern points of the northern hemisphere experience later sunrises and earlier sunsets in the winter, and earlier sunrises and later sunsets in the summer. Any data published in Britain takes British Summer Time into account; so when looking for patterns, allow for anomolies between March and April and between October and November. The times of sunrise and sunset are important to farmers, weather forecasters, sailors and other people.

Preparation
Find tables showing the times of sunrise and sunset. (These are usually given for London and a more northerly city such as Manchester or Glasgow.) Make one copy per child of photocopiable page 126.

Resources needed
A directional compass, weather vane or other directional aid; simple models of the Earth and the Sun; photocopiable page 126; squared paper; pens and pencils; pictures and reference materials relating to the times of sunrise and sunset.

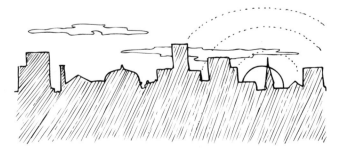

Vocabulary

Sunrise, sunset, daylight, darkness, hours, length, direction.

What to do

If the location and weather are suitable, try to observe the direction in which the Sun rises on several winter mornings. Warn the children about the dangers of looking directly at the Sun, although its strength will be noticeably weaker at this time. Also, observe the direction in which the Sun sets at the end of the afternoon. To identify the directions, the children can use a compass or observe a weather vane or compass points drawn on the playground. Discuss why it is only possible to collect this information at school during the winter; talk about the children's experiences of very early sunrises and very late sunsets. Ask them to draw a diagram to show the apparent movement of the Sun, indicating the direction in which it rises and sets.

Explain that scientists can calculate the times of sunrise and sunset for any particular point on the planet, and that these times vary from place to place in a precise pattern because of the way in which the Earth moves around the Sun. Use models to remind the children of the relative movement of the Earth and the Sun. Show them the tables of daylight information published in diaries and newspapers; look for clear patterns, such as the sunrise times starting the year around 8am and becoming earlier until midsummer, then gradually becoming later again.

Give out copies of photocopiable page 126, which gives some simplified information about the sunrise and sunset times for Glasgow for the beginning of the fourth week of each month. Help the children to interpret the information

and identify any patterns. Remind them that we alter the time twice a year in order to have more light in the mornings in winter; this explains the interruptions in the pattern of times. Ask the children to work out the hours of daylight for each of the months shown and write them on the page, then use them to draw a bar graph (see Figure 15). Ask them to write a sentence describing what the data shows.

Talk about the effect that different amounts of daylight have on our lives. Using any suitable reference materials, discuss people whose work is affected by the amount of daylight: milkmen, postmen, farmers and so on. Consider how people working in industry take darkness and daylight into account: suppliers of electricity and gas, food producers and so on. Talk about countries such as Iceland where the winter is completely dark, and how this affects human activity.

Suggestion(s) for extension

Some children might be interested to compare local sunrise and sunset times with those in more northerly or southerly places. They could also research the sunrise and sunset times in a northerly country such as Iceland. Ask them to find out how much more or less daylight a distant city experiences than one close by.

Suggestion(s) for support

Where necessary, help children to complete the photocopiable sheet by filling in some of the daylight hours (such as those of February, June, July and November); assist with calculating the other daylight hours. Give help with drawing the bar graph where necessary.

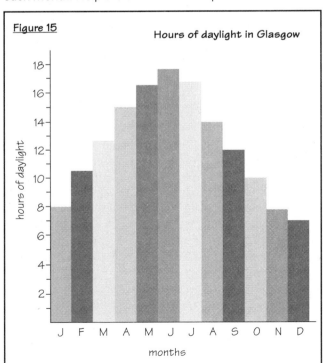

Figure 15

Hours of daylight in Glasgow

hours of daylight (y-axis: 2, 4, 6, 8, 10, 12, 14, 16, 18)

months (x-axis: J F M A M J J A S O N D)

Assessment opportunities

Do the children understand that the Sun rises in the east every day, moves across the sky and sets in the west? Do they recognize that the Sun's path across the sky is shorter in the winter than in the summer? Also focus on the children's ability to draw a graph and use it to identify patterns in the data. Can they write an accurate description of what the data shows? (For example: *The Sun rises earlier every month until June, then it rises later each month until December*).

Opportunities for IT

Using data handling software, data about the times of sunrises and sunsets can be stored, retrieved, interpreted and presented as graphs.

Display ideas

Use two wall areas to represent the shortest day and the longest day. Make large circles to represent clocks, with the hours of darkness shaded; use these as backing for pictures showing the activities, problems and benefits associated with short or long days. Display the children's graphs.

Other aspects of the PoS covered

Introduction (Sc0) 1a, b, c, d; 2a, b; 3b; 4a, c.

Reference to photocopiable sheet

The data given on photocopiable page 126 shows the times of sunrise and sunset in Glasgow at the start of the fourth week in each month. The times are simplified. The children can work out the hours of daylight for each of the days shown, draw a bar graph and look for patterns in the data.

Sunrise and sunset times for Glasgow

Name _____ Date _____

	Sunrise	Hours of daylight	Sunset
January	08.30		16.30
February	07.15		17.45
March	06.00		18.45
April	05.50		20.50
May	05.00		21.30
June	04.30		22.10
July	05.00		21.40
August	06.15		20.20
September	07.10		19.10
October	08.00		18.00
November	08.15		16.00
December	08.45		15.45

YEAR TO YEAR

The Earth takes a fixed period of time to orbit the Sun; we call this period a year. Reference materials can help us to find information about areas of science which we cannot investigate for ourselves.

†† *Whole-class demonstration and discussion; individual recording.*

🕐 *60 minutes.*

Previous skills/knowledge needed

The children should know that the Sun and the Earth are spherical bodies; that although the Sun appears to move across the sky, it is really the Earth which is moving; and that the Earth spins on its axis every 24 hours, causing day and night. They need to understand that although there are many scientific phenomena they can investigate for themselves, they have to acquire other information from secondary sources such as books, videos and CD-ROMs.

Key background information

Astronomers have calculated the distance and shape of the Earth's orbit around the Sun. We refer to the time this orbit takes as one year. During this time, the Earth rotates 365¼ times; thus we have a leap year every four years to account for the extra day.

Preparation

Make one copy per child of each of photocopiable pages 127 and 128.

Resources needed

Models to represent the Earth and the Sun; pictures and other reference materials relating to the Earth's orbit, including information about scientists such as Galileo and Newton; photocopiable pages 127 and 128.

Vocabulary

Sun, Earth, sphere, rotate, rotation, axis, orbit, year, month, season.

What to do

Remind the children of the relationship between the Earth and the Sun: that the Earth is much smaller than the Sun and orbits around it, while also spinning on its own axis. Use models (and, if possible, a video) to show the Earth's orbit around the Sun. Point out the shape of this orbit: an oval or ellipse, not a circle. Ask a group of children to represent the Sun, while a single child rotates and orbits to demonstrate the movement of the Earth.

Ask: *How long does it take for one rotation or spin of the Earth?* Tell the children that after rotating 365¼ times, the Earth has also completed one orbit of the Sun, a period of time which we call a year. Explain that we need to have

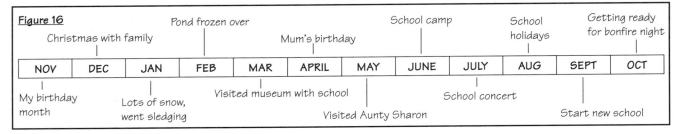

Figure 16

NOV	DEC	JAN	FEB	MAR	APRIL	MAY	JUNE	JULY	AUG	SEPT	OCT

Christmas with family — Pond frozen over — Mum's birthday — School camp — School holidays — Getting ready for bonfire night

My birthday month — Lots of snow, went sledging — Visited museum with school — Visited Aunty Sharon — School concert — Start new school

an extra day every four years, so that our years continue to match the orbiting of the Earth; we call the year with an extra day a 'leap year'.

Point out that it is not possible for us to experience the orbiting of the Earth for ourselves; but that astronomers and other scientists have studied the Earth's movements, made calculations and recorded information which has been used to build up a picture of the Earth's orbit. Show the children a range of reference materials which will help them to understand more about the Earth, the Sun and the nature of planetary orbits.

Discuss what the children understand by *a year*. Emphasize that it is the period of time from any one day of the calendar to the same day a year later, not only from January 1st to December 31st. Ask the children to consider a year of their own life, from their last birthday to the next, thinking about the seasons as well as any major public or personal events. Give out copies of photocopiable pages 127 and 128. The children should use page 128 to draw a personal timeline for one year, using the information on page 127 to help them. Discuss which season each child's birthday belongs to; be aware that the beginning and ends of seasons cannot be defined precisely. Events such as Christmas, holidays and personal anniversaries can be indicated on the timeline. (See Figure 16.)

Finally, ask the children to draw an annotated diagram showing the Earth's orbit, and to indicate how long the orbit takes.

Suggestion(s) for extension

Some children could research the relationship between the tilt of the Earth and the seasons, finding out the meaning of the words *solstice* and *equinox* and including the dates of these seasonal events on their timeline.

Suggestion(s) for support

If children find the information on photocopiable page 127 hard to follow, read it out and explain it as necessary. Make sure the children understand that they should write their birthday month in the first box on page 128, and that they should abbreviate the names of the months.

Assessment opportunities

The children's annotated diagrams of the Earth's orbit will provide evidence of how well they understand what the term *a year* represents. Also note how well they can use secondary information to acquire information.

Opportunities for IT

The children can use CD-ROMs to access information about the rotation and orbit of the Earth, and to research the lives of astronomers and cosmologists.

Display ideas

Keep models and reference materials available for the children, to reinforce their understanding. Arrange a circular display of seasonal pictures to represent the cycle that we experience as the Earth travels through its orbit.

Other aspects of the PoS covered

Introduction (Sc0) 1a, c, d; 2a, 3b, 4a, c.

Reference to photocopiable sheets

Photocopiable page 127 provides background information which the children can use when drawing their own personal timelines; they can use photocopiable page 128 as a framework for this.

Year to year

When the Earth has made a complete orbit of the Sun, we say that a year has passed. Our year is divided into 365 days, which are arranged into 12 months.

December · January · Winter · February · November · March · October · Autumn · Spring · April · September · May · August · Summer · June · July

In the course of a year, we experience four seasons: winter, spring, summer and autumn.

Name

What is the difference?, see page 14

What is the difference? (1)

Name _____   Date _____

▲ A hedgehog and a bat are both mammals.

hedgehog   bat

▲ Write down the differences between these two mammals.

Both oak and holly are leaves of trees.

oak leaves   holly leaves

▲ Write down the differences between oak and holly leaves.

What is the difference? (2)

▲ What are the differences between a hen and a duck?

hen   duck

▲ Cut out the pictures above and the descriptions below.
▲ Match the descriptions with the pictures.

webbed feet for swimming

a pointed beak for pecking food

toes and claws for perching

a smooth head

a rounded beak for scooping up food in water

large tail feathers

a comb on the head

stubby tail feathers

In the garden

A small, spiky animal was snuffling around my garden at dusk. It did not hurry away as I approached, but became quite still. When I moved back into the shadows, it continued on its search for long, juicy minibeasts that wriggled up to the surface of the lawn under the cover of darkness. Only just above my head, dark furry shapes fluttered back and forth, silently sifting their prey from the warm summer air. Shining my torch among the strawberry plants, I was pleased to see at least five pairs of large eyes staring at me from among the wet leaves. I left them to continue their hunt for food. The only sound to be heard was a weird screeching from a feathery outline in a nearby tree.

During the day, the aerobatic swooping is taken over by feathered flyers, which must constantly catch food to satisfy the brood of chicks chirping in their mud nest under the eaves. I notice the nettles by the shed have nibbled leaves, so I search carefully and find groups of hairy, black, wriggling creatures munching furiously. On other plants, I am not so pleased to find hundreds of tiny, green minibeasts which I know are sucking the life out of my favourite blooms. However, I see that their spotted red and black enemies are marching along the stems towards them. In the holes and cracks beneath the stones of the path, armies of soft, damp, legless bodies with huge appetites for juicy, young leaves are waiting for darkness to fall.

Living on a rocky shore, see page 19

A rocky shore (1)

Name _____   Date _____

Low tide

What will happen at high tide?
▲ Draw the plants and animals when the shore is covered with water.

High tide

SCIENCE KEY STAGE TWO

Living on a rocky shore, see page 19

A rocky shore (2)

Name _____ Date _____

▲ Next to each picture, write down how the plant or animal is suited to living on a rocky shore.

limpet	
sea anemone	
crab	
bladderwrack	
kelp	
sea slater	
seabird	

Harmful micro-organisms, see page 23

Micro-organisms

Before they knew that micro-organisms existed, people did not understand what made them ill. They could see the effects that diseases had on them, but they had no idea that these diseases were caused by tiny living things which were too small to be seen.

Louis Pasteur, a French scientist working 130 years ago, was fascinated by the strange living organisms he could see through his microscope. He realized that they must be everywhere in the air, in water and in soil. He called them 'microbes', a word which means 'small life'. Pasteur discovered that microbes feed, grow and reproduce very rapidly. He showed that those living in milk cause it to go sour. He provided evidence to prove that microbes spread easily through the air, but can be killed by heat.

When Joseph Lister, a British surgeon, heard about Pasteur's work, he realized that microbes were causing the deaths of many of his patients. People with wounds soon died because doctors did not know that micro-organisms in the air were entering the wounds and causing infections. Lister started treating the wounds of his patients with strong carbolic acid. This killed any microbes, but also prevented the skin from healing quickly. He improved his method by spraying the air around the patient and then making sure that his own hands, clothes and instruments were also sterilized.

Pasteur was the first person to show that different microbes cause different diseases. Other investigators continued Pasteur's work, so that we now know which micro-organisms (sometimes called germs, bacteria or viruses) cause particular common illnesses, and how we can prevent many diseases from spreading.

98

Plants provide food, see page 26

Food from plants

Name _____   Date _____

▲ Next to each food, write down what part of a plant it has come from.
Use the list of words at the bottom of the page to help you.

rhubarb _____   beetroot _____

hazelnuts _____   beans _____

tomatoes _____   cauliflower _____

pears _____   onions _____

lettuce _____   cherries _____

celery _____   broccoli _____

peas _____   swede _____

carrots _____   cabbage _____

leaves	roots	bulbs
seeds	flowers	fruits	stems

Plants need water, see page 28

Investigating plants and water

Planning

▲ What do you want to find out?

▲ What is your idea for an investigation?

▲ What plants and equipment will you need?

▲ Why is it important to use a large number of plants?

▲ How will the test be organized?

- What will you keep the same?
- What will you change?
- What observations will you make?
- What measurements will you collect?

▲ What are your predictions?

- Do you think all the seedlings in a tray will grow the same?
- Which tray of seedlings do you think will grow the best?

Collecting evidence

▲ Describe how you carried out the test.

▲ How did you make useful observations and careful measurements?

▲ Were there any problems?

Considering evidence

▲ What are the differences between the trays of seedlings?

▲ What do your observations and results tell you?

▲ Is this what you thought would happen?

▲ Can you explain why some plants grew better than others?

Skeletons, see page 36

Animals with skeletons

▲ Look carefully at these drawings of skeletons. What clues do they give about the animals to which they belong?

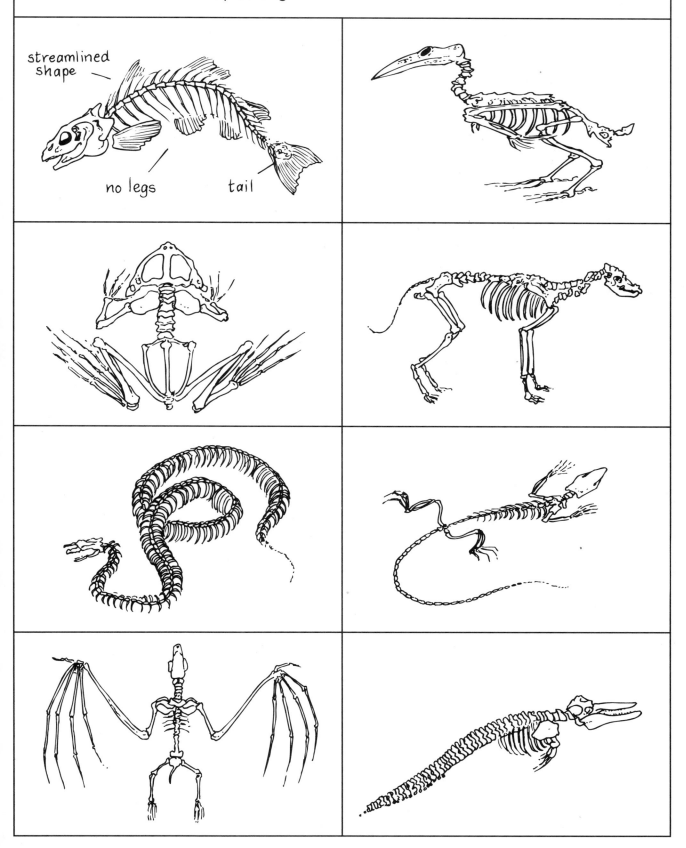

Growing bones, see page 37

Investigating the growth of bones

Our bones continue growing from babyhood through to adulthood.

Planning
▲ Think of a good idea for investigating the differences in the sizes of different people's bones.

▲ Make a prediction which you will be able to test.

▲ Decide what measurements you will need.
  • Describe how you will take these measurements.
  • Decide how many different people's measurements you will need.

▲ Draw a chart for collecting your measurements.

Obtaining evidence
▲ Carry out the test efficiently, making sure that all measurements are accurate.

Considering evidence
▲ Use your results to make a bar chart.

▲ Describe what the bar chart shows.

▲ Does this match your prediction?

▲ Write a sentence to explain what you have discovered.

Using materials, see page 41

Using materials

▲ How many different materials can you see in this picture?

▲ Make a chart to show the materials, their uses and the reasons why they are used.

Using materials, see page 41

A choice of materials

Name _____ Date _____

Sometimes the same object can be made of different materials.

▲ Write down the advantages and disadvantages of the materials used in each pair of objects.

plastic, glass  	
paper, plastic 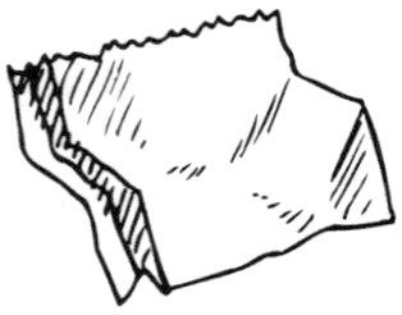 	
wood, metal 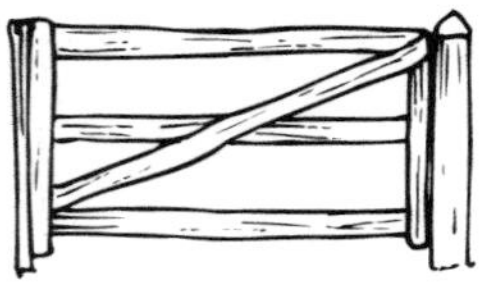 	
plastic, cardboard 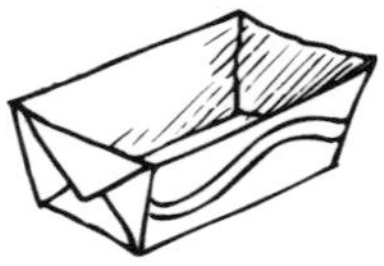 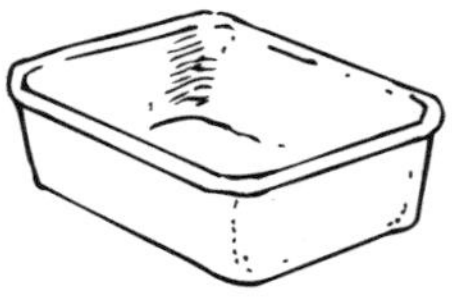	
plastic, metal  	
paper, fabric 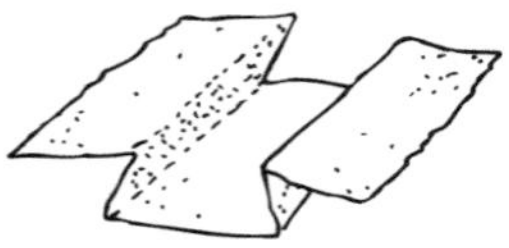 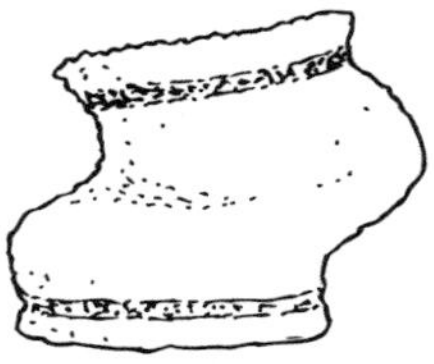	

SCIENCE KEY STAGE TWO

Comparing materials, see page 43

Comparing materials

Planning
▲ What do we want to find out?

▲ Describe the equipment and materials we will use, and how we will organize the test.

▲ What observations will we make?

▲ What measurements will we take?

▲ How will we make sure the test is fair?

- What will we keep the same (the constants)?

- What will we change (the variable)?

▲ Prepare a chart to record your results.

▲ Record your predictions.

Obtaining evidence
▲ Carry out the test safely.

▲ Make careful observations and accurate measurements, so that your evidence is reliable.

Considering evidence
▲ Use the results of the test to draw a bar chart.

▲ What do the results show?

▲ Do you think your test has provided reliable evidence?

▲ Do the results match your predictions?

Rocks of the Earth, see page 45

Rocks of the Earth

The Earth is made up of stone – hard and firm, soft and gritty, shiny and smooth. Stone has been formed by volcanoes, earthquakes and the action of water. It has been laid down layer by layer, covered with ice and weathered through the ages.

The rocks of the Earth are beneath our feet. We see them where there are cliffs, mountains, seashores and small islands. We find water-worn pebbles, once-buried fossils and fire-formed crystals. Looking closely, we see many colours and patterns, and wonder how the rain, sun and frost can have shaped the small ancient stones we have picked up. People have always taken rocks from the earth to build their houses and to make tools, weapons and adornments. They have dug deeper, making mines and quarries to find more coal, limestone, metals and gems.

Over millions of years, rocks have been split by the frost, worn by the wind and baked by the sun until a layer of soil is formed in which trees can grow and crops can be planted. The rock layers are also covered by our houses, roads and cities, all of which use rocks. Buildings may have smooth slate for their roofs, and limestone or sandstone (which are easy to cut) for their walls. Attractive marble is used for statues and decoration, and granite – a very hard rock – is used for steps and harbour walls. Metals also come from the Earth's rocks; clay is shaped and baked to make bricks; sandstone is ground up to make glass, and limestone to make cement.

The rocks of the Earth are mined and cut, sliced and carved, chiselled and chipped, ground up and sanded smooth. They are climbed, decorated and admired.

Solids or liquids?, see page 50

Solids or liquids?

Name _____   Date _____

▲ Decide whether these items are solids or liquids. Then use ticks to show whether they behave as solids or liquids normally do.

Item	Solid or liquid?	Does it have a definite shape?	Can it be poured?	Is it easy to hold?	Does it need a container to hold it?
a chair					
vinegar					
a newspaper					
sand					
a plant pot					
soil					
beads					
fruit juice					
talcum powder					
salt					
petrol					
a ruler					

▲ Sort the items:

solids	solids behaving like liquids	liquids

Solids to liquids, liquids to solids, see page 52

Solids to liquids; liquids to solids

Name _____   Date _____

Solid or liquid?	Process and temperature change	Examples
chocolate  solid	melts as the temperature rises	
wax		
water		
metal		
molten lava		

Air all around

Name _____   Date _____

▲ Squeeze a sponge under water. Write down your observations.

▲ Pour water over a sample of soil. Describe what you see.

▲ Complete these sentences. The words in the box will help you.

Air is _____

Air can _____

Bubbles of air _____

The holes in the soil are _____

escaped from the sponge.	full of air.
move into very small spaces.	all around us.

Liquids to gases, see page 55

Investigating evaporation

Name _____   Date _____

Planning notes

Our question about evaporation:

My predictions:

Equipment and materials we will use:

Observations and measurements we will take:

What we will keep the same:

What we will change:

▲ Prepare a chart for your results.

Changing state

▲ Explain the changes of state in each picture. Use some of the words below.

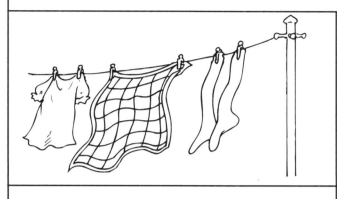 

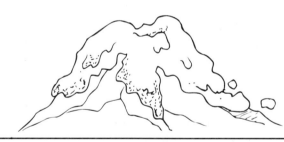 

 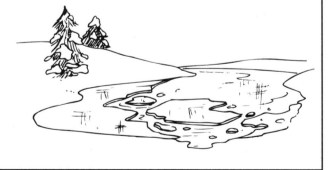

freeze	freezing	melt	melting	evaporate
evaporating	evaporation		condense	condensing
condensation	solidify	solidifying		solidification

How pure is water?

Name _____ Date _____

▲ Examine each water sample carefully. Predict whether it is pure or contains dissolved materials.
▲ Evaporate the samples. Record your observations and explanations.

Sample of water	Predictions	Observations	Explanations
tap water			

SCIENCE KEY STAGE TWO

Reversible and irreversible changes, see page 60

Reversible and irreversible changes

Important vocabulary

mix	dissolve	solidify
mixing	dissolving	solidifying
mixture		solidification

cools	melts	freezes	burns
cooling	melting	freezing	burning

evaporates	condenses	filters
evaporating	condensing	filtering
evaporation	condensation	filtered

solid	liquid	gas

temperature rises	temperature falls

reversible change	irreversible change

chocolate	cement	salt	
sugar	water	ice	wood
sand	water vapour	wax	

Waste materials

Every day each one of us throws something away – a sweet wrapper, a banana skin, a drinks container. Getting rid of rubbish is a problem. When our bins are emptied, the waste is taken away to a disposal site which is usually a hole in the ground, perhaps an old quarry. However, we are running out of large holes in the ground, and not many people like rubbish tips near their homes.

Some materials that we no longer need are biodegradable, which means they are attacked by micro-organisms, are rotted away and become part of the soil. Others are durable, which means that they are long-lasting. This may be useful while we need them, but makes them difficult to get rid of when we don't need them. One answer to the rubbish problem is to recycle more waste and keep our dustbins empty.

Garden rubbish and kitchen waste can be made into compost and used to enrich the soil, which will grow more plants. Paper is biodegradable, but we create so much waste paper that it can be collected to be used again. Instead of producing all our new paper from the wood of trees, a proportion is made from treated waste paper. Glass and plastic items, such as bottles, can be melted and remoulded into new products.

Metals have always been reused. They are sorted into different types, heated in furnaces until they are soft or liquid, then shaped and hammered into new objects. Even small items such as drinks cans consist of valuable metal, which should be recycled rather than discarded.

Vehicle tyres are a big problem. They need to be replaced regularly for safe driving – which means heaps of disused rubber. Unfortunately, no-one has yet found a good use for old tyres; and they cannot be burned, as they produce poisonous gases which pollute the air.

Other things that we no longer need might be useful to other people. Unwanted clothing is collected by charities and sent overseas. Wood from various objects can be used again or burnt as fuel.

If everyone sorted and recycled their waste materials, fewer of the Earth's limited resources would be used up, and our landscape would be saved from a covering of rubbish.

Waste materials, see page 61

What can we do with waste?

Name _____   Date _____

Rubbish	Material	Durable or biodegradable	Alternatives to waste disposal
	plastic		
	glass		
	rubber		
	wood		
	fabric		
	metal		
	paper		
	vegetable waste		

The brightness of bulbs, see page 63

Investigating the brightness of bulbs

Name _____   Date _____

Observations	
Predictions	
Change made to the circuit	

Slide away, see page 68

Investigating movement along surfaces

Name _____   Date _____

Planning notes

Describe what you want to find out, what you will do, and what you will use.

What are your predictions?

What evidence will you collect?

How will you make sure that the test is as fair as possible?

▲ Prepare a chart for your results.

High and low friction, see page 70

Friction

Name _____   Date _____

▲ Look carefully at each picture. Decide whether high friction or low friction is important.
▲ Write down an explanation for each case.

Water resistance, see page 71

Water resistance

Name _____   Date _____

▲ Compare the movement of different shapes through water.

Draw and describe each shape	Observations	Time taken to reach bottom of jar

Spring is here, see page 73

Useful springs

Name _____   Date _____

▲ Explain why springs have been used in each of these objects.

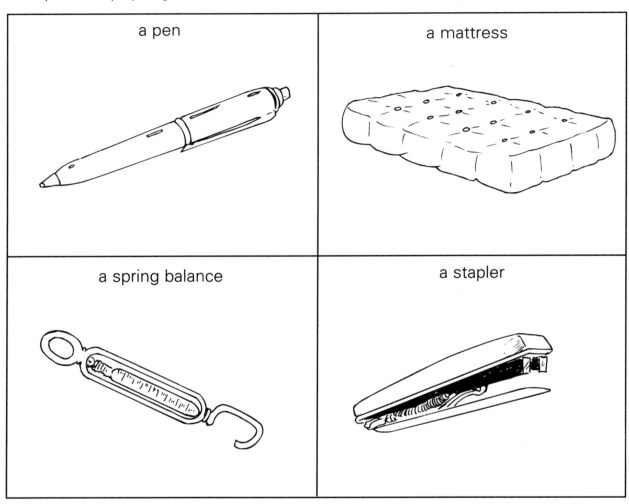

a pen	a mattress
a spring balance	a stapler

▲ Choose two other examples of objects that use springs. Draw and describe them below.

Balanced forces, see page 76

Balanced forces

Name _____   Date _____

When an object is stationary, the forces acting on it are balanced.
▲ Draw arrows on these pictures to represent the forces.
▲ Describe the forces in each picture.

Weight in air and water, see page 77

Weighing in air and water

Name _____   Date _____

▲ Use a force meter to weigh objects, first in air and then in water. Record your measurements.

Object	Weight in air	Weight in water

▲ Write down comments on your results. How can you explain them?

Transparent and opaque, see page 79

Investigating transparent and opaque materials

Name _____ Date _____

Observations	
Predictions	
Material or object	

How we see things

Name _____   Date _____

▲ Draw arrows to show how the people in these pictures can see things.

▲ Draw and label a diagram to show how you are able to see this page.

Changing shadows, see page 82

Investigating how shadows change

Name _____   Date _____

Planning notes

What we want to find out:

▲   Describe, with the help of a diagram, what you will do.

What we will keep the same:

What we will change:

What measurements we will take:

Sunrise and sunset, see page 89

Sunrise and sunset times for Glasgow

Name _____ Date _____

	Sunrise	Hours of daylight	Sunset
January	08.30		16.30
February	07.15		17.45
March	06.00		18.45
April	05.50		20.50
May	05.00		21.30
June	04.30		22.10
July	05.00		21.40
August	06.15		20.20
September	07.10		19.10
October	08.00		18.00
November	08.15		16.00
December	08.45		15.45

FURTHER *Curriculum Bank* ACTIVITIES
PHOTOCOPIABLES

Year to year

When the Earth has made a complete orbit of the Sun, we say that a year has passed. Our year is divided into 365 days, which are arranged into 12 months.

In the course of a year, we experience four seasons: winter, spring, summer and autumn.

Year to year, see page 91

A year of my life

Name _____   Date _____

From my last birthday on _____ to my next birthday on _____, the Earth has completed one orbit around the Sun.